MARCONI AND WIRELESS

PLATE I

Guglielmo Marconi

MARCONI AND
WIRELESS

BY

R. N. VYVYAN

EP PUBLISHING LIMITED
1974

Republished 1974 EP Publishing Limited
East Ardsley, Wakefield
Yorkshire, England

with the kind permission of the
copyright holders.

First published by Routledge and Kegan
Paul in 1933 under the title
"Wireless Over Thirty Years".

The publishers wish to acknowledge the
help and co-operation given by GEC-Marconi,
Chelmsford, Essex.

ISBN 0 7158 1050 2

Please address all enquiries to EP Publishing Limited
(address as above)

Printed in Great Britain by
REDWOOD BURN LIMITED
Trowbridge and Esher

CONTENTS

Contents

LIST OF ILLUSTRATIONS

DIAGRAMS

FOREWORD

In writing this book, especially where it deals with aspects of wireless development with which I have not been personally in touch, I have drawn upon information contained in various publications, to the authors and publishers of which I wish to take this opportunity of expressing my indebtedness.

I owe particular thanks to the Marchese Marconi for permission to use information contained in the various papers he has from time to time read before various learned societies. In connection with the work of the early pioneers, previous to Marconi, Mr. Ellison Hawk's interesting book *Pioneers of Wireless*, published by Messrs. Methuen and Co., has been especially valuable, as has also Mr. J. J. Fahie's well-known work, *A History of Wireless Telegraphy from 1838 to 1899*.

The early chapters of the present book deal with the developments of wireless on the long wave system up to the successful establishment of commercial transatlantic wireless, and illustrate the difficulties, disappointments and triumphs of Marconi's early pioneer work. Technical descriptions have as far as possible been deliberately avoided ; for those interested in descriptions and illustrations of the apparatus and circuits used, I recommend Sir Ambrose Fleming's *Principles of Electric Wave Telegraphy*, also Mr. H. M. Dowsett's book, *Wireless Telegraphy and Broadcasting*. I owe grateful thanks to Sir Ambrose Fleming for the loan of his original notes regarding the early experiments at Poldhu and the research done by him leading up to his invention of the thermionic valve.

I wish to express especial thanks to Colonel A. G. Lee, the Engineer-in-Chief of the Post Office for the valuable information given me regarding British Post Office wireless development.

For the information given in the chapters devoted to Wireless in the War I am particularly indebted to Colonel

C. J. Aston and Lieut.-Colonel H. B. T. Childs. In connection
with the chapters on broadcasting, I have received valuable
assistance from Mr. Noel Ashbridge, the Chief Engineer of
the British Broadcasting Corporation.   I also gratefully
acknowledge the help accorded me by Marconi's Wireless
Telegraph Co., Ltd., Imperial and International Communications, Ltd., and the Marconi International Marine
Communication Co., Ltd., and the ever ready assistance
that I have received from a number of my former colleagues,
particularly Capt. J. M. Furnival, Mr. J. A. Smale, Mr. A. W.
Ladner, Mr. J. C. Robb, Mr. N. Wells, Mr. H. M. Dowsett,
Mr. P. J. Woodward, Mr. J. Brown, and Mr. C. E. Rickard.

R. N. VYVYAN.

WIRELESS OVER THIRTY YEARS

CHAPTER I

EARLY PIONEERS

FROM the time of the Greek and Roman civilization until the last two hundred and fifty years, science in its important branches of chemistry, biology, medicine, mechanics and electricity made little progress. Since that period an astonishing advance has been made, due to the discoveries of the great scientists of the seventeenth and eighteenth centuries. Their work opened up new fields of exploration, which resulted in a rapid increase of invention in every branch of science. The mechanical and industrial development of the world, the reduction of suffering, the prolongation of human life and the improvements in the comfort and amenities of modern existence are all due to the work of these early pioneers.

There is romance in the achievement of all human endeavour. The triumphs of success are not attained without much drudgery and many failures. The conception of an idea may, after a long period of gestation, give birth to a new process, which, after years of development, may fundamentally alter the amenities of civilization. The genius who invented the wheel lived before the period wherein there is any historical record, yet his invention has, without doubt, done more to advance civilization than any other that can be named.

Great discoveries or inventions are rarely arrived at by accident. The inspiring idea is the result of a train of thought, due to the earlier work of others, possibly in some different field of research. Each pioneer cuts his way a little further into the forest of ignorance, and the path to knowledge proceeds, sometimes slowly, sometimes more rapidly, until

A

at length some man breaks through into a clearing, where a wider horizon is visible, and another step forward to the ultimate goal is achieved.

Discoveries in science are often made in advance of the requirements of the time, but inventions are rarely made except to meet the existing needs of civilization.

The rapid industrialization of the world in the early nineteenth century by the invention of the steam engine, brought about its application to railway and steamship transport. The speeding up of communications by this means cheapened the cost of materials, and raised the purchasing power of the nation, thus enabling more goods to be manufactured and sold. The rapid increase in trade pointed to a growing need for quicker methods of the transmission of intelligence, and thus the invention of the electric telegraph at once fulfilled an existing need.

The rapid transmission of intelligence by various methods has been practised from the most ancient times. In the Bible reference is made to the use of pillars of fire by night, and columns of smoke by day. The earlier settlers in America found that this means of conveying intelligence was practised by the American Indians. To come nearer home—The summons to arms, at the time of the Spanish Armada, by means of beacon fires on well-known heights throughout the country, is a familiar fact to every school child.

Among savage nations the use of drums for signalling has long been practised. By this means they are able to broadcast from tribe to tribe any news of interest with astonishing speed. It is said that no European has as yet been able to interpret the meaning of the signals or the nature of the code used, but the messages are quite clear to every native in the district where the sound of the drum is heard.

It was not until the end of the eighteenth century that any mechanical contrivance was invented to telegraph information. These devices were known as semaphores : they consisted of wooden arms revolving on a centre post, and the position of the arm or arms relative to the post signified a letter of the alphabet. Semaphore telegraphs were first erected in France in 1793, and in England in 1795 between London and Dover. These were set on heights about 8 miles apart, and it was possible to send a message from London to Dover in ten minutes.

The invention of the electric telegraph quickly superseded all mechanical and visual devices : its use was rapidly developed, and a network of telegraph wires soon spread over the land, connecting all towns and villages together.

Countries separated from one another by sea were however still without means of international communication and this need was met by the invention of the submarine telegraph or cable. The first cable was laid across the Straits of Dover, in 1850, and consisted of a fine copper wire insulated by a thick coating of india-rubber. It was not a success, as the insulation was soon destroyed. A new cable was put down in 1851. Profiting from the experience gained, the insulation of this cable was protected with a sheathing of iron wires wound around it, and finally covered by windings of jute. This cable is actually still used up to the present day. In the development of this new invention new problems had to be faced, electrical and mechanical, and it was found that the speed at which intelligence could be conveyed through a cable was much slower than over a landline wire supported by poles. This was due to the much greater capacity of a cable per mile, which so distorted the signals that each had to be of longer duration to be intelligible, with the consequent result that the longer the cable the slower was the speed of signalling through it.

Modifications in design and in the materials used and improvements in the terminal apparatus gradually increased the speed of operation until it was possible to consider the construction of a cable across the Atlantic as a commercial enterprise. The first Atlantic cable was laid in 1858, but broke down after a few signals had passed, and commercial communication was not satisfactorily established until 1866, when a new cable was laid down. From that date, until the triumphant success of beam short wave wireless communication, new cables were continuously being installed to establish new services or supplement existing ones. Thus by the time when wireless had at last proved itself a serious rival to existing cable communication, a world system of cables had been built up, connecting the most distant parts of the world and forming a thoroughly reliable and efficient means of communication. While cables could connect distant countries, there was no means of establishing communication with ships at sea, or with other moving objects; there was therefore a need for wireless, in its primary application, before its invention became possible.

The invention and development of wireless telegraphy will for all time be associated with the name of Marconi. It was the study of the work of the earlier pioneers and investigators on electro-magnetic radiation, and the application of the theories they propounded, that convinced Marconi that a system of telegraphy through space could be provided by means of electric waves. When Marconi revisited Bologna, where he was educated, on the thirtieth anniversary of the granting of his first patent, in a speech he stated " From my youth, I would almost say from my boyhood, the experimental discovery of electric waves made by Hertz, in confirmation of the mathematical hypothesis of Clerk-Maxwell regarding the electro-magnetic theory of light, and the brilliant pursuit of such researches made by our great Bolognese physicist Augusto Righi had fascinated my mind. I soon had the idea, I might say almost the intuition, that these waves might, in a not distant future, furnish mankind with a new and powerful means of communication utilizable not only across continents and seas, but also on board ships, bringing with it a vast diminution of the dangers of navigation and the abolition of the isolation of those crossing the sea."

Before describing the methods Marconi devised by which he realized his ambition, it is advisable to refer to the work of those pioneers who influenced Marconi in his early experiments, and of whose work he had knowledge :—Clerk-Maxwell, Hertz, Righi and Branly.

Clerk-Maxwell, after a brilliant university career and after various professorial appointments, became Professor of Experimental Physics at Cambridge. He studied closely Faraday's work and in 1855 read a paper on " Faraday's Lines of Force." Faraday had propounded the theory that the electrical interaction between two bodies was conveyed by lines of force through the ether, and was not explicable by the old " elastic solid theory of light." Clerk-Maxwell showed that electrical and optical phenomena are mani-

PLATE II

JAMES CLERK-MAXWELL

HEINRICH RUDOLF HERTZ

[By permission of The Exclusive News Agency

PROFESSOR AUGUSTO RIGHI   PROFESSOR EDOUARD BRANLY

[face p. 4

festations of the properties of one single medium, in which two physical states can be established, called "Electric Strain" and "Magnetic Flux." Examining the fundamental relations of these electric and magnetic qualities mathematically, Clerk-Maxwell found that they led to equations of the same type as those which express wave motion through a continuous medium, and that their effects therefore must be propagated in space with the same velocity as light. As a corollary therefore, he proved that light was merely a form of electro-magnetic waves, identical physically with electric waves. This masterly mathematical treatise resulted in the foundation of the electro-dynamic theory of light. Many scientists, however, were reluctant to accept this new theory and abandon the old one of action at a distance, but universal acceptance of the electro-dynamic theory resulted after the work of Hertz became known.

The experiments of Hertz proved that the behaviour and measurements of electric waves corresponded exactly in every particular to Clerk-Maxwell's prediction. Clerk-Maxwell's discovery is the more remarkable in that he proved the existence of electric waves solely by logical mathematical reasoning; he had no means or knowledge either how to generate or receive them, but he opened up a new field for research, the result of which has led to such stupendous developments.

Hertz was born in 1857 and studied at Munich with the intention of taking up engineering as a profession. He soon found that the physical theories upon which engineering is based were of more interest to him than their mechanical application. He therefore changed the course of his studies. In 1878 he went to the Berlin University and became a pupil of the famous scientist Helmholtz. He was soon employed on original research work. In 1883 he went to Kiel as Professor of Theoretical Physics, devoting much time and study to the elucidation of Clerk-Maxwell's electro-magnetic theory. It became clear to him that if a conducting body is charged or discharged suddenly, electrical waves must be emitted into the ether. Hertz, when giving a lecture, was experimenting with two flat coils and a Leyden jar. He observed that the discharge of the jar through one coil, provided that there were a small spark gap in this coil, induced a current in the other coil, although there was no connection between the coils. This led him to make his famous series of investigations. His apparatus for radiating and receiving electric waves was remarkably simple. His transmitter or, as he called it, " Exciter " consisted of two metal plates connected by rods to two metal spheres separated by about half an inch. The rods were connected to the terminals of the secondary winding of an induction coil. When the coil was energized a spark or train of sparks jumped across the gap between the two spheres. The receiver or, as Hertz called it, the " Resonator " consisted of a piece of wire bent into a circle, the ends of the wire terminating in two small metal balls, thus forming a circular loop with a small gap in it ; the length of this gap could be adjusted by a micrometer screw. The resonator was set up at a short distance from the exciter, and when a spark jumped across the space between the balls of the exciter, a spark was also seen to pass across the small gap in the resonator. With this apparatus Hertz carried out a large number of investigations. He reproduced electro-magnetically, and in rapid succession, all the phenomena of light, and thus completely demonstrated that light was a form of electric wave. He perceived that his experiments confirmed Clerk-Maxwell's theory. He pointed out that when sparks passed rapidly at the exciter, rectilinear oscillations were radiated into the surrounding space. The resonator was brought into all kinds of different positions in relation to the exciter, and the results accurately measured and tabulated. Hertz found that the law of radiation was the same as the corresponding law in optics. In further experiments he proved that the velocity of electric waves is the same as that of light, differing only in length of wave and penetrative power. He found that they could be reflected and even polarized, that they are propagated in straight lines, but that they cannot pass through metal screens, the presence of which causes electrical shadow effects. Hertz was the first to produce a generator of electric waves, as well as to demonstrate their physical properties. As Sir Oliver Lodge has stated, " he effected an achievement that will hand his name down to posterity as the founder of a new epoch in experimental physics." Hertz's discoveries were studied in the laboratories of many different parts of the world, and improved methods of generating and detecting electric waves were soon effected.

Important contributions to the development in this branch of physics were made by Augusto Righi, Professor of Physics at Bologna University. Hertz had used waves from 30 centimetres to many metres in length : Righi was able to propagate waves as short as 2.5 cms. He found that the smaller the exciter balls, the shorter the wavelength. He effected several improvements in the Hertz oscillator ; he placed the spark gap in thick vaseline oil, and found that this made the production of the waves more consistent and regular. He also invented a new detector. This was effected by cutting thin lines on the back of a mirror, thus dividing the metallic surface into narrow discontinuous strips.

Righi's contribution to the development of the generation and detection of electric waves is not in itself so important as the work of some others, but it is particularly mentioned here, as it was through Professor Righi's influence that Marconi was greatly attracted to the study of the Hertzian waves.

The resonator as used by Hertz, while serving admirably the purpose of his experiments, was an extremely inefficient detector. It was obvious that an instrument of much greater sensitivity was needed before Hertzian waves could be put to practical use. Many forms of detectors have been devised ; amongst others Lodge invented one consisting of a metallic needle resting on a plate (incidentally this, slightly modified, was used at a later date by Marconi in his transatlantic experiments as an atmospheric leak, across the much more sensitive receiver which by that date had been invented). The most sensitive detector, however, was of the microphonic type, in the special form invented by Professor Branly and afterwards greatly modified by Marconi.

Branly, when he invented the coherer known by his name, was Professor of Physics at the Catholic University in Paris. The principle of coherence of minute particles of metal under an electric pressure was already known. Onesti, an Italian Professor, had discovered that copper filings piled up between two metal plates were normally non-conductors of electricity, but became conductive when subjected to a high voltage spark discharge. Previous to Onesti's discovery, S. A. Varley in England made the first practical application of the principle of cohesion in utilizing fine charcoal powder as a leak for lightning discharge, the powder being a non-conductor of electricity until caused to cohere by the action of a lightning flash.

Branly made a series of investigations into the variations of conductivity of a large number of materials under different electrical influences. He found that substances which responded best to the phenomenon of sudden increase of conductivity were iron, copper, brass, aluminium, zinc, and similar metals. He discovered that the conductive effect on metallic filings, caused by a near-by electrical discharge, persists for a comparatively long period, but disappears rapidly if subjected to a shock. He obtained this result therefore by tapping the tube in which the filings are contained : he thus discovered a principle which was adopted in the original Marconi system. Marconi acknowledged his debt to Branly, and after his successful experiments in wireless telegraphy across the Channel he sent Branly a Marconigram reading " Marconi sends M. Branly his respectful compliments across the Channel this fine achievement being partly due to the remarkable researches of M. Branly."

The four scientists whose contributions to the discovery have been very briefly sketched, were not the only men who did valuable work in this new field of research. They have been particularly mentioned on account of the influence of their work in attracting Marconi to experiment in this field of investigation. Reference must be made, however, to Hughes, Lindsay, Willoughby-Smith, Dolbear, Popoff, Elihu Thomson and Lodge, all of whom can be cited as early pioneers in wireless research.

The brilliant work of Sir Oliver Lodge cannot, however, be passed over without further mention. He closely followed and verified Hertz's experiments and conclusions. At the British Association meeting in 1894, he demonstrated the efficiency of a coherer of the Branly type as a detector of electrical waves up to a distance of 150 yards. He showed how,

PLATE III

[*Photo by Elliott & Fry*

SIR OLIVER LODGE

[*face p.* 8.

on depressing the key at the transmitter, a perceptible signal was recorded at the receiver. Lodge states that " signalling was easily carried on from a distance through walls and other obstacles, an emitter being outside and a galvanometer detector inside a room. Distance is not very easy to get in a town and stupidly enough no attempt was made to apply any but the feeblest power so as to test how far the disturbances could really be detected." In an article in *Wireless Weekly*, 26th Sept. 1923, Lodge explained his failure to realize the possibilities offered in the following words, " I was too busy with teaching work to take up telegraphic or any other development, nor had I the foresight to perceive what has turned out to be its extraordinary importance to the Navy, the Merchant Service, and indeed land and war services too."

Lodge confined his work to experiments in the laboratory and Lecture Room, but later, when Marconi had taken out his first master patent, Lodge showed that some degree of privacy could be attained in wireless, and unwanted messages eliminated to a certain extent, by tuning the transmitter and receiver. He took out a patent for this, which was acquired by the Marconi Company at a later date.

Nearly all the development and research work leading up to the invention of wireless telegraphy has been done by professors. The chief aim of their research and experiments has been to acquire further knowledge, and advance the cause of science another step. They have laboured often without reward, beyond the remuneration they received as professors, imparting their knowledge to the students under them. Their time was sufficiently occupied in their academic duties, and their research work was generally done in their few hours of leisure. The possibility of developing their discoveries for commercial purposes seldom occurred to them. It remained therefore for a young man, a mere youth, to seize the great opportunity offered, and with consummate intuition and skill to put his finger on the missing links and co-ordinate the work already done into a result of incalculable value to mankind.

CHAPTER II

MARCONI'S EARLY WORK

IN the previous chapter it was stated that Clerk-Maxwell put forward the theory, and Hertz proved by practical experiments, that light is a form of electro-magnetic radiation. Further that long electric waves, as used in wireless telegraphy, travel at exactly the same speed as the very short waves of light and follow the same laws of reflection, refraction and polarization. Our senses are, in fact, extremely delicate receivers of electro-magnetic waves. The eye is intensely sensitive to a certain band of frequencies which we know as light, while our sense of feeling responds to the longer etheric vibrations of heat. The still shorter light waves, known as ultra violet rays, while not visible to the eye, have greater penetrating power, and are detectable by other means. On the lower scale of the light band frequencies the infra red rays have recently been used for photography at great distances, where the ordinary light rays would be unable to give a clear picture. All forms of electro-magnetic radiation can truly be said to be forms of wireless, when they can be recorded either by the senses, or by some chemical, electrical, or mechanical means. There is nothing more mysterious in wireless telegraphy than the response of the eye to light vibrations, and the manner in which the information received by the eye is relayed to the brain. Lord Kelvin therefore aptly described a wireless telegraph receiver as an " electric eye." Of the sixty-four octaves in electro-magnetic radiation the waves which produce the sensation of light are all contained within one octave, the average wavelength of which is one fifty-thousandth of an inch, or about 600 million times shorter than the average wavelength used in broadcasting. The invention of wireless telegraphy is the discovery of means of producing, and controlling electro-magnetic waves and methods of recording them. Hertz had shown how these could be produced by the disruptive discharge of a spark, but the electric eye had not in his time been developed.

We come therefore to the brilliant work of Marconi.

Guglielmo Marconi was born at Bologna on 25th April 1874. His father was an Italian country gentleman who, in 1864, married Miss Annie Jameson, daughter of Mr. Andrew Jameson, of Daphne Castle, County Wexford, Ireland. Marconi is therefore half Italian, and half Irish.

Marconi was privately educated at Bologna, Florence and Leghorn. As a boy he took a keen interest in physical and electrical science. He studied physics under Professor Rosa of the Technical School at Leghorn and made himself thoroughly acquainted with the works of Professor Righi, thus obtaining much knowledge of Hertzian wave research. He had definitely come to the conclusion while still a student that it should be possible to devise means whereby use could be made of the propagation and reception of electric waves for the purpose of telegraphing signals, and he decided to devote his attention to this study.

Consider the romance of this young man's life ! Whilst most young men of his age have ideals and ambitions, which they hope will fructify, few of them harness their ambitions to matters of an impersonal nature. Marconi hitched his wagon to an unknown star of the first magnitude, the light from which had as yet been only dimly perceived. Due to his intuition and painstaking investigation, its radiance has grown rapidly brighter and brighter, until at length it has illuminated the whole earth, to the benefit of all mankind. Imagine the gift to the blind of the now universal broadcast of music. Even the humblest cottager is enriched by the boon of this development of wireless, which brings the best instrumental and vocal music of Europe to every home. Furthermore, those who listen to the broadcast programmes, and those listeners are now the majority of the population in most countries, have the very best lectures on matters of general interest. They hear the news of the day, and they hear the spoken thoughts on literature, politics, and modern culture by the best contemporary authorities. A young man dreamed a dream and woke up to find that it was true. Marconi brought his dream to realization, and his contribution to the sum total of human endeavour brought him the Nobel Prize for Physics in 1909.

The many thousands of lives saved at sea, due to wireless, the great increase in the facilities of communication, and the many other applications of wireless due to his inventions, have resulted in making his name one of the most honoured, not only in his own era but for all time.

The perversity of human nature is such that it delights to reward with its highest distinctions those who have been the most successful in destroying human life, and to describe the rise to fame of such great Generals as an epic of romance. The greatest scientists of the past, unlike the successful soldier, rarely during their lives had more than a local reputation, and in several cases were imprisoned or tortured for describing the results of their discoveries. Had Marconi lived in those times he would certainly have been condemned to death as a magician. In our more enlightened age he has received distinctions which in their quality and quantity have never previously been bestowed on any other scientist. Marconi's early work is worthy of detailed description.

His first efforts were made in 1894, before he was 21, at his father's country estate in Pontecchio, near Bologna, across a distance of only a few yards in a room. He started his experiments with an induction coil as a Hertzian emitter, using at first the ball discharger designed by Professor Righi, consisting of 4 brass balls, separated by small gaps, and immersed in vaseline oil. In order to control the discharge across the spark gap he inserted a Morse key in the primary circuit of the induction coil. He was thus able to cause long or short trains of sparks to jump across the spark gap corresponding to the length of time the Morse key was held down. This gave means of controlling the radiation from the emitter to follow predetermined signals sent on the Morse key. Marconi soon found the space indoors was not sufficient to enable him to carry out his experiments satisfactorily, and he removed his apparatus to the garden, where tests could be carried out over greater distances. He soon made a most important discovery. Instead of using the two rods of Hertzian oscillator, he connected one terminal of the secondary of the induction coil to a metal cylinder, or capacity, elevated to the top of a pole, and the other to a metal plate laid on the ground. He thus produced an elevated aerial which discharged across the spark gap to the earth. At the receiving end he erected a similar capacity on the top of a pole and connected it to earth through a Branly coherer. He found that the Branly coherer was neither sufficiently sensitive nor reliable in its action, so he devoted his attention to improving this instrument. Branly and others had used rather long tubes, with a considerable quantity of somewhat coarse filings. Marconi eventually adopted a much smaller tube, about 5 mm. diameter and about 3.5 centimetres long. He reduced the gap between the plugs in which the filings were placed to about 2 mm. of each other. He made the plugs of silver and arranged that they should fit tightly into the tube; the ends of these plugs were highly polished and slightly amalgamated with mercury. Connections to the plugs were made with platinum wire, and were brought out of each end of the tube. After a series of investigations as to the best metals for the filings he chose a mixture of nickel and silver, in the proportion of 95 per cent nickel and 5 per cent silver, and these filings were carefully sifted to a certain degree of fineness. The space in the tube between the two silver plugs was about $\frac{1}{3}$ to $\frac{1}{2}$ filled with these filings and the glass tube was then exhausted of air and sealed. Subsequently the ends of the plugs were made wedge shaped, so that the tube could be turned to different positions to vary the width of gap between the two plugs within which the filings rested.

This coherer was a far more sensitive and reliable detector of electric waves than anything that had as yet been developed. Having devised a coherer that would respond to very weak impulses, it was necessary to arrange means to restore the coherer to a non-conductive state immediately after coherence. Marconi therefore arranged a circuit consisting of the coils of a sensitive relay, with a single dry cell in series with the coherer, so that when the coherer became conductive, the circuit of the relay was closed. The coils of the relay were wound with a resistance of 1000 ohms to ensure that a current not greater than one milliamp would pass through the coherer. The closing of the relay closed the circuit of the tapper coils, the tapper being designed on the principle of an electric bell, the coherer tube taking the place of the bell gong. The hammer of the tapper was arranged to strike upwards against the coherer, and means were provided for adjusting the force of the blow from the tapper so that the most sensitive adjustment for coherence and decoherence could be effected. Marconi also found it necessary to insert two choking coils in the leads to the coherer, to prevent the oscillations set up by the minute sparks at the tongue of the relay and tapper travelling back to the coherer. The relay, besides working the tapper, was also arranged to work a telegraph printing instrument, so that the signals received could be recorded. The whole of this apparatus with its battery of dry cells was mounted on a wooden base and placed in a metal box, to protect it from the action of stray sparks or oscillations.

While making the various important improvements to the detector above described, Marconi was at the same time carrying on a systematic series of experiments to ascertain in what way the height to which he elevated his capacity affected the distance at which his detector would respond. In 1895 he employed metal cubes about one foot square, erected on poles two metres high, and found that with similar arrangements at both ends, he could receive signals at 30 metres distance. On doubling the height to four metres, the distance of reception was increased to one hundred metres; again doubling the height to eight metres the range became four hundred metres. Marconi's next step was to increase the size of the cubes to about three feet three inches square, and with this new aerial he was able to record Morse signals at a distance of about one and a half miles.

In addition to these experiments on elevated capacities, Marconi endeavoured to effect greater distances by concentrating the transmitted wave in the required direction. To effect this he placed the discharge balls of the transmitter in the focal line of a cylindrical parabolic metal reflector, and the receiving detector in the focus of a similar reflector. This was the genesis of the invention which gave birth to the beam aerials of later days, when short waves became practicable, and years after Marconi's patent for reflectors had run out.

PLATE IV

GUGLIELMO MARCONI

At the time of his first experiments in England

[face p. 15

Marconi came to England and applied for a British patent for his apparatus in 1896, which was duly granted. In July 1896 he brought his invention to the notice of Sir William Preece, who was then Engineer-in-Chief of the British Post Office, and who had himself developed a system of wireless telegraphy by the conductive-inductive method. Sir William Preece arranged that every facility should be granted to the young inventor to demonstrate his invention, and his system was successfully operated between the General Post Office and the Thames Embankment.

A diagram of the circuits of the transmitter and receiver he was then using is given in Fig. 1 of the Appendix.

The experiments which first drew the attention of the public to the importance of the invention were those carried out on Salisbury Plain, in the presence of representatives of the Navy, Army and Post Office, when reception over a distance of eight miles was demonstrated.

In June 1897 Sir William Preece gave a lecture at the Royal Institution on " Signalling through space without wires," and after expounding other and older methods, including his own, he exhibited Marconi's apparatus and, referring to its capabilities, he said :—

" In July last Mr. Marconi brought to England a new plan. Mr. Marconi utilizes electric or Hertzian waves of very high frequency. He has invented a new relay, which for sensitiveness and delicacy exceeds all known electrical apparatus. The peculiarity of Mr. Marconi's system is that, apart from the ordinary connecting wires of the apparatus, conductors of very moderate length only are needed and even these can be dispensed with if reflectors are used."

At the conclusion of his lecture he combated the contention put forward by certain people that Marconi had done nothing new in these words :—

" He has not discovered any new rays, his recorder is based on Branly's coherer. Columbus did not invent the egg but he showed how to make it stand on its end, and Marconi has produced from known means a new electric eye, more delicate than any known instrument, and a new system of telegraphy that will reach places hitherto inaccessible. . . . Enough has been said to show that for shipping and lighthouse purposes it will be a great and valuable acquisition."

The widespread publicity given to the successful demonstrations caused the greatest interest, not only to the general public, but also in scientific circles. In Germany Professor A. Slaby, of the Technical High School at Charlottenberg, Berlin, who had been experimenting on Hertzian waves, came to England and obtained permission to witness a demonstration of the new invention.

A series of demonstrations was arranged to take place between Penarth and Weston-Super-Mare, at which Professor Slaby was present, and at which satisfactory reception was effected over a distance of nine miles. Marconi showed the Professor all his apparatus and explained to him the experiments which led up to the results he had obtained. As a result of what he saw in these tests Professor Slaby wrote an article on the " New Telegraphy " which appeared in the *Century Magazine* in 1898 and from which the following remarks may be quoted :—

" In January 1897, when the news of Marconi's first successes ran through the newspapers, I myself was earnestly occupied with similar problems. I had not been able to telegraph more than 100 metres through the air. It was at once clear to me that Marconi must have added something else—something new—to what was already known, whereby he had been able to attain to lengths measured by kilometres. Quickly making up my mind, I travelled to England, where the Bureau of Telegraphs was undertaking experiments on a large scale. Mr. Preece, the celebrated Engineer-in-Chief of the General Post Office, in the most courteous and hospitable way, permitted me to take part in these, and in truth what I saw there was something quite new. Marconi had made a discovery. He was working with means the entire meaning of which no one before him had recognized. Only in that way can we explain the secret of his success. In the English professional journals an attempt has been made to deny novelty to the method of Marconi. It was urged that the production of the Hertz rays, their radiation through space, the construction of his electric eye—all this was known before. True ; all this had been known to me also and yet I never was able to exceed 100 metres. In the first place, Marconi has worked out a clever arrangement of apparatus, which by the use of the simplest means produces a sure technical result. Then he has shown that such telegraphy (writing from afar) was to be made possible only through, on the one hand, earth connection between the apparatus and, on the other, the use of long extended upright wires. By this simple but extraordinary effective method he raised the power of radiation in the electric forces a hundred fold."

It is interesting to note that Marconi had taken out patents in Germany for his invention, but a year later patents were granted to Professor Slaby, who had modified the aerial circuit as patented by Marconi, and he, in collaboration with Count Arco, developed what was known as the Slaby-Arco system. This in 1903 was amalgamated with the Braun, Siemens and Halske systems, and the German national wireless system known as the Telefunken system was thus formed.

Continuing the early history of the development of wireless, Marconi gave successful demonstrations in July 1897 of his system to the Italian Government. Apparatus was installed on two warships and communication established up to a distance of 12 miles.

After these various demonstrations of the reliability and usefulness of the invention, " The Wireless Telegraph and Signal Company Limited " was formed (in 1897) to acquire Marconi's patents in all countries except Italy and her dependencies, where Marconi had already made special arrangements in return for the assistance rendered to him by the Italian Government. Subsequently (in 1900) the name of this Company was changed to Marconi's Wireless Telegraph Company Limited.

Marconi's next step was to erect a station at Alum Bay in the Isle of Wight, and another at Bournemouth. For this communication he elevated his aerials to a height of about 120 feet and used a 10-inch spark induction coil. The working of this station was inspected by many prominent people, among them Lord Tennyson and Lord Kelvin, and it is worthy of record that the first two paid wireless messages ever sent were from this station. Both were sent by Lord Kelvin, one to Sir William Preece at the General Post Office, on 3rd June 1898, and the other to Sir George Stokes.

The rapid advance made by Marconi in his work is shown by the fact that within two years of his having sent his first signal over distances of a few yards, the range had been increased from yards to miles. He had proved that wireless telegraphy could be worked by night as well as day, in fogs

B

or storms as well as in fair weather, and that high hills and other obstructions did not prevent communication. It had also been proved that the apparatus could be worked by the ordinary telegraphist and was not costly to construct.

Very early in his experiments Marconi found that greater ranges could be spanned over sea than over land. As it was precisely over sea that existing means of communication were inadequate, the sea was clearly the first natural sphere for the utilization of wireless telegraphy, and the earliest demonstrations of its real practicability were made in Italian waters, and around the coast of the British Isles.

In May 1898, at the request of Lloyds Corporation, apparatus was installed at Ballycastle and Rathlin Island, in the north of Ireland ; uninterrupted communication was obtained, and the apparatus was worked by Lloyds lighthouse keepers, who were not long in learning how to use it.

In July of the same year the Wireless Company was requested by a Dublin newspaper (the *Daily Express*) to report from the sea the results and incidents of the Kingston Regatta. A steamer, *The Flying Huntress*, was equipped for this purpose, and over 700 messages were sent and received during the course of the Regatta. This was the first instance where a ship had been equipped for commercial purposes.

On the 3rd of August 1898 wireless communication was established between the Royal Yacht *Osborne* and Osborne House, Isle of Wight, in order that Queen Victoria might communicate with the Prince of Wales, who was suffering from the results of an accident to his knee. Constant and uninterrupted communication was maintained during the sixteen days the system was in use ; the messages, about 150 in number, were private communications between the Queen and the Prince.

Marconi throughout his career has directed much attention to increasing the distance over which reliable communication could be effected. With the apparatus he used from 1896 to 1898 he found that the maximum distance that could be covered seemed to increase in proportion to the square of the height of the aerial wire. Thus, if he doubled the height of the aerial, the range of the communication possible would be four times as great as before. There were obvious difficulties in increasing the height of the aerials used, and if no other improvement was practicable the range of wireless was likely to be limited by the height to which it was economically possible to elevate the aerial. Marconi therefore studied the possibilities of improvements in the sensitiveness of his receiver. Marconi was well aware that in his system at that date there was one particular cause of inefficiency, namely, the position of the coherer in the aerial circuit. It was clear to him that, with an elevated aerial having its lower end connected to an earth plate, when the fundamental oscillation is set up in the aerial, there would be a node of potential, or anti node of current, at the lower end of the aerial, and that therefore there could only be a very small difference of potential across the coherer, which could only be placed near the earthed end of the aerial. Marconi solved this difficulty by inserting in the aerial in place of the coherer the primary winding of a small air core transformer ; the secondary windings of this were split by a condenser, the outer ends being brought to the terminals of the coherer, while the ends connected to the condenser led to the coils of the relay. Many forms of these transformers or, as they were called, jiggers were made before an efficient design was produced, and it was found that the length of the windings of the secondary circuit had to bear a certain definite relation to the length of wave used. The employment of this new device, which was patented, increased the sensitiveness of the receiver very substantially and considerably increased the range of the apparatus, and encouraged Marconi to attempt to communicate across the Channel.

The introduction of the Receiving Jigger is shown diagrammatically in Fig. 2 of the Appendix.

In the Spring of 1899 the French Government gave permission to erect a mast for experimental purposes at Wimereux, near Boulogne, and a corresponding mast was erected at the South Foreland lighthouse, near Dover. The stations were completed in March, and Marconi transmitted messages across the Channel for the first time on 27th March 1899. The successful result created immense and universal public interest, and the importance to the shipping interests was generally accepted. Letters were received from all over the

world, some asking for information, some giving advice, and
many from cranks and madmen who attributed the illnesses
from which they suffered to the passing of the wireless waves
through their bodies. An amusing case occurred at Wimereux,
which, had it not been for the tact of the Engineer-in-Charge,
Mr. W. W. Bradfield, might have been a tragedy. A man
burst into the wireless room brandishing a revolver and
stating that the wireless waves gave him intense internal pains
and unless the engineer stopped the apparatus he would shoot
him. Mr. Bradfield at once expressed his sympathy, and
told him he had heard of other people who had been similarly
inconvenienced but he had come to the right man to cure
him and all that was necessary was a form of electrical
inoculation. If he would consent to receive a shock from the
aerial he would be immune from the effect of electric waves
for ever after, but he must first put aside any metal coins
he might have in his pocket and, of course, a large piece of
metal like the revolver. The man at once agreed, he was
given a very severe shock but went away happy and con-
tented. This incident remains in the writer's mind as a
singular example of tact and coolness in a sudden emergency.

Rapid increases in the range of wireless stations took place
after the bridging of the English Channel. The Wireless
Company had established their Works at Chelmsford and
had erected a mast there 150 feet high. Communication was
effected between this station and Wimereux without difficulty,
the distance being 85 miles, of which 55 miles were over land.

In the same year Marconi went to the United States and
reported the progress of the International Yacht Races from
a ship to the shore ; over 4000 words were sent in less than
five hours' work done on different days. A more important
test of the system was however made during the Naval
Manoeuvres of the British Navy in the autumn of 1899.
Two cruisers were equipped, and important orders were sent
by wireless up to a range of 85 miles. These demonstrations
definitely established the importance of wireless telegraphy
both for naval and mercantile marine purposes.

Contracts with large transatlantic shipping companies and
agreements with Lloyds Corporation for the establishment of
coast stations, and regular and permanent services between

ship and ship, and ship and shore, were soon after concluded by the Wireless Company, while the British Admiralty made its first purchase of 32 installations.

From the experience gained in the early days of the commercial use of wireless telegraphy, it was recognized that some means must be found of ensuring selectivity of reception. Up to the year 1900 the simple form of detector, before the introduction of the receiving " jigger," was non-selective, that is to say, it was sensitive to electric waves varying greatly in wavelength, in fact a single electro-magnetic impulse, if strong enough, would affect the receiver. Sir Oliver Lodge pointed out in 1897 the importance of tuning the transmitter and receiver to the same wavelength, for securing privacy of communication. Early in 1900 Marconi made a fresh advance. Hitherto the energy utilized in signalling had been that which could be stored up in the aerial itself. The amount so stored was comparatively small, and consequently the waves sent out at each discharge of the spark were rapidly quenched. Marconi took out a patent for " tuned or syntonic telegraphy, as well as for multiplex telegraphy with a single aerial." This patent became famous in litigation as the four sevens patent (its number was 7777) and its validity was upheld in the High Court. The important novelty in the patent was the incorporation of tuned closed with tuned open circuits, in both transmitter and receiver. As the methods described in this patent are of such fundamental importance, and cover the whole principle of tuning up to modern practice, it is desirable to describe at some length the circuits used (see Appendix).

The provision of a closed circuit coupled to, and in tune with, the open aerial circuit, enables the aerial to draw off gradually the energy stored in the closed circuit, which serves as a reservoir of energy. It is clear that a much more persistent train of oscillations is set up in the aerial at each discharge than in the case where the storage of energy is that due to the aerial only. When the circuits are accurately tuned, electrical oscillations set up in the closed circuit create other sympathetic swings in the aerial circuit, and each train of waves consists of a much larger number of waves, slowly decreasing in amplitude. In other words a long slightly damped train of waves rather than the quickly quenched train of the original arrangement. The receiver, also provided with tuned circuits, and tuned to exactly the same wavelength, is influenced by the sustained weak impulses received, and in its turn imparts the received energy to the closed condenser circuit in association with it.

The receiving circuits can be set in electrical vibration better by a large number of electric waves, even of weak impulse, arriving on the receiving aerial at intervals exactly corresponding to the natural period of the vibrations of the receiving circuits themselves, than by a single impulse or solitary wave. Hence with an accurately tuned receiver, although the ether may be full of electric waves impinging on every aerial, the receiver will only respond to the wavelength to which it be tuned, provided the other impulses be not too powerful.

Marconi realized this important principle of his invention, and consequently that it would be possible to attach two or three transmitters to one aerial, and two or more receivers on one receiving aerial, providing they were tuned to wavelengths substantially different from each other. He gave demonstrations of multiplex reception in 1900 and in 1901 used the arrangements as shown in Figs. 5 and 6 for sending messages from St. Catherine's, in the Isle of Wight, to the Lizard over a distance of 156 miles.

PLATE V

CIRCLE OF MASTS ERECTED AT CAPE COD, U.S.A., BY MARCONI WIRELESS
TELEGRAPH CO., LTD.

[face p. 23

CHAPTER III

POLDHU AND NEWFOUNDLAND EXPERIMENTS

THE information contained in the previous chapter deals
with the very early work of Marconi up to the beginning
of 1900, when he took out his famous patent for syntonic
wireless telegraphy. The experiments and developments
which have been so far mentioned have been obtained either
from written records of contemporary happenings or from
first-hand information, imparted to the Author by the
Marchese Marconi himself, or one of his assistants.

Early in 1900 the Author joined the staff of the Wireless
Telegraph and Signal Co., Ltd., and he had the good fortune
to be closely associated with Marconi from that date, when
the induction coil was still the only transmitting generator
and the coherer the form of detector used in the receiver,
and to have assisted him in the many developments that
have taken place during the past thirty-two years. It will
therefore perhaps be forgiven if a personal note, and the
personal pronoun should from now on occasionally intrude.

On appointment to the Technical Staff I was sent to the
Chelmsford Works, and after a short period to become
familiar with the simple transmitter and receiver then used
I was employed, with most of the other assistants, in designing and testing different forms of receiving "jiggers."
It had been found necessary to reduce the capacity between
the primary and secondary windings of the jigger and a form
of jigger was then evolved with the secondary windings pile
wound, as shown in Fig. 7, in the Appendix.

The Author was responsible for a different type, which
consisted of three pancake wound coils, mounted on a glass
rod, the centre coil being the primary winding and the two
outer coils the two secondary windings. These latter could
be slid backwards or forwards on the glass rod, thus varying
the mutual inductive capacity between the two windings and

their coupling at will. This form of jigger was not then adopted, but is interesting as it was the first variable loose coupled oscillation transformer made up to that time, and its principle has now been adopted in modern practice. After this period at the works I was sent to the wireless station at Dovercourt, to obtain experience in operating and maintaining a wireless telegraph station. At stations built in those early days the mast supporting the aerial was similar to a ship's wooden mast, and consisted of a lower mast, top mast and topgallant mast, to use sea phraseology, and if still greater height was required a top spar called a royal mast. All these had to be individually stayed to the ground, but to avoid the effect of metal stays on the radiation from the aerial, these stays were made of hemp or manilla rope. Every time it rained the stays contracted in length and they had therefore to be slacked off, whereas as soon as the sun had dried them they had to be tightened up : it was a relief therefore to the station staff when rope stays were superseded by steel wire stays, insulated at intervals by porcelain insulators.

By the year 1900 the technical staff that the Wireless Company had collected numbered only seventeen. Among these several have since become well known in technical circles. Mr. W. W. Bradfield, C.B.E., the late General Manager and Director of Marconi's Wireless Telegraph Co., Ltd., and of the Marconi International Marine Communication Co. Ltd., was one of this small band. Other well-known names comprise Dr. W. H. Eccles, F.R.S., who later became President of the Institution of Electrical Engineers, and an authority and well-known writer on the theory of wireless ; the late Dr. Erskine Murray, who became well known as an author on wireless problems and as a consulting engineer ; Mr. Andrew Gray, who became the first Chief Engineer of the Marconi Company ; and the present Engineer-in-Chief, Mr. C. E. Rickard ; while Mr. C. S. Franklin's name is well known for his important contributions to research, and for his valuable inventions, and particularly in connection with short wave practice and the development of the Beam Aerial and Reflector. All were very enthusiastic and realized that they were assisting in the development of a new industry.

The rapid increase in the range of wireless communication and the fact that Marconi had been able to telegraph satisfactorily up to a distance of 150 miles, convinced him that the curvature of the earth presented no obstacle to the extension of wireless communication to still greater distances. He therefore decided to make a serious attempt to telegraph by his system across the Atlantic. Although Marconi had shown that increasing the height of the aerial increased the range of signalling in proportion to the square of the height, the practicable economic height of wooden masts for supporting the aerial was at that time thought to be about 200 feet. (It was not thought wise to use steel masts or towers until a much later date.) Hence the conclusion he arrived at was that transatlantic wireless could only be accomplished by the radiation of much greater energy than could be obtained from an induction coil and battery of Leyden jars, and that therefore the transmitter would have to be designed as an engineering plant of considerable power, yet arranged so as to be safe to use.

The Wireless Company in 1899 had appointed Professor J. A. Fleming, F.R.S., of University College, London, as Scientific Adviser to the Company, and knowing the experience that Dr. Fleming had gained in dealing with extra high tension alternating currents in electric lighting work, Marconi consulted him in regard to the nature of the electrical plant it would be necessary to instal to generate and control the powerful electro-magnetic waves he required. They decided that it would be necessary to employ an alternator, driven by an engine, and actuating high tension transformers in order to charge a bank of condensers, which would discharge through an oscillation transformer across a spark gap, and they further agreed that the alternator should have an output of 25 kilowatts. Marconi entrusted Dr. Fleming with the working out of the details of this plant, and to devise some method of interrupting the primary circuit of the transformers to allow of signalling at will. It was decided that the station for the transatlantic experiments should be built on the west coast of Cornwall in some isolated place, to avoid the possibility that the powerful electrical oscillations might affect electric circuits used for lighting or other purposes in the neighbouring district, and also in order that there should be no obstacle to the clear passage of these waves over the ocean in the immediate vicinity of the station.

Owing to the experience that I had had, previous to joining the Wireless Company, of power station practice and in engineering works, it was my good fortune to be selected to take charge of the construction of this station and to assist Dr. Fleming in obtaining the necessary machinery and plant. In July 1900 I accompanied Marconi and the Managing Director of the Wireless Company, Major Flood Page, to Cornwall, where a site was selected at Poldhu, near Mullion, on the West Coast of the Lizard.

Meanwhile Dr. Fleming had been busy working out the details of the high tension plant and designing the power condensers for the installation, and I was employed in assisting him, until possession of the site was obtained early in October 1900, whereupon I returned to Poldhu to supervise the work.

To get signals across the Atlantic Marconi had calculated that he would require a capacity of 1/50th of a microfarad discharging across a two-inch spark gap. One of the many problems was to obtain this by the single action of a transformer on a condenser without raising the transformer voltage to an unworkable value. Dr. Fleming thereupon devised a method of double transformation, whereby the current from a transformer was employed to charge a condenser, discharging through an oscillation transformer across a spark gap. The secondary of the transformer, consisting of more turns than the primary, was connected to a second spark gap, a second condenser and the primary winding of a second oscillation transformer being also across this spark gap. The secondary of the last transformer was in series with the aerial. This arrangement is shown diagrammatically in Fig. 8 (see Appendix).

The effective working of this arrangement depends of course on the proper syntonization of each circuit. But the principles of syntonization were by this time thoroughly understood, largely as a result of Marconi's work on Syntonic Wireless Telegraphy.

Another important problem requiring solution was to

devise a satisfactory method of signalling. It must be remembered that to design a transmitter one hundred times more powerful than the type used up to this date involved the careful consideration of every detail of the plant. Syntonic wireless entails resonance between circuits, and great care had to be taken to prevent voltage peaks due to resonance from getting back into the transformers and alternator, and causing surges which might break down the insulation. Any method of signalling by which the transformer is suddenly connected to, or disconnected from, a condenser might give rise to this condition. Dr. Fleming devised several methods but the first practicable method, used in the first tests at Poldhu, was quite a simple one. It consisted in the insertion in one of the leads from the alternator to the transformer of the high tension winding of a 20 kw. 2000 to 200 volt transformer. The low tension winding was connected, through a large key, with a water resistance. The closing or opening of the key altered the impedance of the alternator transformer circuit and thus slow signalling was possible. The arrangement used is shown in Fig. 9 of the Appendix.

After the first satisfactory signalling tests were made with this method in use, Dr. Fleming replaced the regulating transformer by a choking or impedance coil, and by short-circuiting this coil it was possible to signal without breaking such large currents, and thus at a considerably higher speed.

By the middle of January the building at Poldhu had been completed, and the plant all installed, ready for the first tests to ascertain if the first electric wave power station ever built, would function according to calculations. Dr. Fleming came to the station on 22nd January, and systematic tests took place step by step which were sufficient to show that the work was being conducted on the right lines. During the next four months much work was done by Marconi and Dr. Fleming in modifying and improving details of the oscillatory plant. Marconi made a great improvement in the design of the oscillation transformers, which hitherto had not been efficient, and a series of satisfactory tests were carried out between Poldhu and the Isle of Wight. Early in February I was recalled to London, and informed that I had been selected to build a similar station to that at Poldhu in America.

Up to that time no aerials except of a temporary nature had been erected at Poldhu, and while in London I was shown the design of a mast system it was proposed to erect at Poldhu, and was told that I should have the responsibility of erecting a similar one in America. This mast system consisted of a ring of 20 wooden masts, each 200 feet high, arranged in a circle 200 feet in diameter. It was intended to support a conical aerial of 400 wires, each wire insulated at the top and connected at the bottom, thus forming an inverted cone. The mast system did not appear mechanically sound, as each mast was stayed to the next one and only to the ground in a radial direction to and away from the centre of the mast system. I criticized the design accordingly but was overruled and instructed to erect them in America as designed. I sailed for America with Marconi and he selected a site for the American corresponding station at South Wellfleet, Cape Cod, Massachusets. He then returned to England, leaving me to make the necessary contracts and construct this station. The work proceeded rapidly and by the end of June I had completed the circle of masts and the buildings, a view of which is given in the illustration facing this chapter. It was clear to me, however, that the mast system was distinctly unsafe. In August, under the influence of nothing more than a stiff breeze, the heads of the masts on the windward side bent over to a dangerous degree, and I reported this to the London Office, asking permission to lower the royal masts for safety. Meanwhile a similar ring of masts was being erected at Poldhu, but before the system was completed the masts collapsed during a gale on 17th September 1901, and the masts at Cape Cod suffered a like fate a few weeks later. When the masts at Cape Cod fell, one mast penetrated the roof of the transmitting room, while another fell within three feet of where I was standing at the time, but neither at Cape Cod nor at Poldhu was there, fortunately, any loss of life. At Poldhu Marconi quickly erected two masts and put up an aerial of 54 wires, spaced 1 metre apart and suspended from a triatic stay stretched between these masts at a height of 150 feet ; the aerial wires were arranged fan shaped and connected together at the lower end. After numerous tests and experiments with this makeshift aerial, Marconi determined to see if he could record the signals from the Poldhu station on the other side of the Atlantic.

The arrangement of the transmitting plant at Poldhu had been somewhat modified from the arrangement shown in Fig. 9, the regulating transformer had been replaced by two signalling chokes, and other accessories for protecting the various circuits from the effects of high frequency oscillations had been inserted. The actual arrangement used is shown in Fig. 10, in the Appendix, where also the actual values of the various circuits as finally adjusted by Marconi are given. Marconi had made tests using this arrangement of plant with his most distant station at Crookhaven, on the west coast of Ireland 225 miles away, and the strength of the signals there received was so great that he felt confident they would be of observable strength at ten times the distance. He decided to make his first tests in Newfoundland, the nearest part of the Western Hemisphere to the British coast. As the step he was taking represented such a sensational extension of the existing range of wireless he wisely decided to keep secret the real object of his mission. He reasoned that if he stated his purpose beforehand and failed, it would throw some discredit on his system in its more modest scope, whereas if he succeeded the success would be all the greater by reason of its total unexpectedness. Marconi left England on 27th November 1901, taking with him two assistants, Mr. Kemp and Mr. Paget, and arrived at St. Johns, Newfoundland, on 5th December. He received every assistance from the Governor, Sir Cavendish Boyle, and from Sir Robert Bond, the Prime Minister. They placed a room at his disposal in a Government building at Signal Hill and Marconi thereupon set up his apparatus.

On 9th December Marconi cabled to Poldhu to begin the prearranged programme, consisting in sending the Morse letter S (a succession of three dots) from 3 p.m. to 6 p.m. each day, and signals began to be sent out in this manner on Wednesday 11th December. In Newfoundland the balloon had been inflated but it broke away on its first ascent and was lost. On Thursday a kite carrying an aerial wire was successfully hoisted to a height of 400 feet. The kite was rising and falling in the wind throughout the experiments and varying the electrical capacity of the aerial. It was impossible to use, thereiore, any form of syntonic apparatus and Marconi was obliged to employ the next best means at his disposal. He therefore used a highly sensitive self-restoring coherer of Italian Navy design, simply connected in series with a telephone and the aerial, and with this simple receiving apparatus on Thursday, 12th December 1901, he and one of his two assistants heard the faint S signals. He had transmitted a recognizable signal across the Atlantic for the first time, and demonstrated that an electric wave, generated by a power not exceeding 12 kilowatts, with an aerial only 150 feet high, could traverse the Atlantic and retain sufficient energy at a distance of 1800 miles to influence the simple receiver he was able to employ.

This achievement created an immense sensation in every part of the civilized world, but soon the voices of the doubting Thomases were heard. A number of technical papers suggested that Marconi had mistaken atmospheric disturbances for the letter S. Mr. Edison, interviewed on the achievement, said " Let us not forget that there are such things as strays." The general form that criticism took was that the world had only Marconi's unsupported word that he had achieved this wonder, and that of his two assistants. A moment's reflection will show how fallacious was this reasoning. To secure himself against the evil effects of failure absolute secrecy was essential. The first day the signals were of unmistakable strength, the second day they were weaker. It required the keen ear of the trained operator to detect them. He found that he could not use the syntonic recording receiver owing to the continuously varying capacity of the aerial in the wind, and he had to depend therefore on an untuned aerial circuit, for which he used a special coherer directly connected to a delicate telephone. In the circumstances it was obvious he could have no other evidence but his own observation, but the fact that he had pledged his own scientific reputation to the accuracy of his statements should have been a sufficient answer to such criticisms. He explained that, in the first place, he was desirous of determining the scientific truth that electric waves could be radiated of sufficient strength to cross the Atlantic. He had next to consider the simplest yet unmistakable signal that could be so transmitted. He was faced with many new difficulties—extreme distance, the type of receiving apparatus he could employ, which had necessarily to be of a simple nature under the conditions of the test, possible atmospheric disturbances when using a long receiving aerial attached to a balloon or kite, storms, and other matters of technical detail. To attempt too much at the start might be to ruin all, and he wisely confined his efforts to the constant repetition of the simplest signal. He stated that the signals received were somewhat weaker than he had anticipated but that the results obtained convinced him that commercial transatlantic wireless telegraphy could now be shortly achieved. His experiments in Newfoundland were brought to an abrupt conclusion by the receipt of a notice from the Anglo-American Telegraph Company stating that they had a monopoly in Newfoundland of all telegraphic communications, and that he must cease his operations. The Canadian Government at once invited him to Canada, where he received the utmost encouragement. He was offered a substantial subsidy to build a station on the Canadian coast, and in February 1902 an agreement was made and ratified by the Canadian House of Commons granting a sum of £16,000 for the erection of such a station, on condition that the wireless rates for telegrams sent across the Atlantic should not exceed 10 cents a word. The Canadian Government by this far-sighted and public spirited action, in the cause of technical advancement and public welfare, played a very large part in bringing about the remarkable developments in long-distance wireless communication which took place during the next few years, because it was at the Canadian station erected at Glace Bay, Cape Breton Island, that most of the experimental work that led to a regular transatlantic service originated, and it was from this station that the first wireless transatlantic messages were successfully transmitted.

Marconi after his visit to Ottawa returned to England via New York. While in the United States he came to South Wellfleet and inspected the station, which I had then completed except for an aerial system. Marconi instructed me to return to England to assist him in the plans he would have to consider for the proposed Canadian station, and informed me that he wished me to supervise its construction and operation.

In February 1902 Marconi thought it desirable to test how far messages transmitted by the powerful station at Poldhu could be detected on a ship. The ship selected was the S.S. *Philadelphia* of the American Line and the results obtained during the voyage were of great scientific importance. The receiving aerial was fixed to the top of the mast, which was about 170 feet high. As the aerial was fixed, and not attached to a kite floating up and down, as in the Newfoundland experiment, a syntonic receiver could be used and the signals recorded on tape. Marconi sailed on this ship towards the end of February. I had taken the opportunity of my brief holiday in England to get married, and my wife and I accompanied Marconi on this memorable voyage. On the start of the voyage the ship was in communication with the ordinary short range coastal station in the Isle of Wight up to a range of 70 miles, after which Poldhu was tuned in. Readable messages were recorded on tape up to a distance of 1551 miles from Poldhu, and signals, the famous letter S, were recorded up to 2099 miles. For purposes of comparison, tests were also made using the self-restoring Italian Navy coherer, as in the Newfoundland experiments, but it is of interest that with this coherer 700 miles was the limit of distance. These results, attested by Captain Miles of the *Philadelphia*, confirmed even in the minds of the most sceptical the accuracy of Marconi's statements with regard to the Newfoundland tests. The most important scientific discovery made on the voyage, however, was that electric waves, as then used, travel farther at night than at day. At distances of over 700 miles signals transmitted in daylight failed entirely, while at night they were quite strong at 1550 miles. Had Marconi known of this phenomenon when in Newfoundland and carried out night tests the results he would have achieved would have undoubtedly been more convincing. The voyage proved that, with a similar station to Poldhu in service on the American coast, shipping equipped with suitable receivers could be kept in touch with the shore throughout the voyage across the Atlantic. Marconi has always been an optimist, as all men who believe in progress must be, and on arrival in New York he stated that, given adequate apparatus, he thought it would be possible to send a message entirely around the world, to start the message eastward around the globe and to receive it again at the same station from the westward. Years passed but eventually in 1926 his prophecy was fulfilled when the short wave beam stations were erected, and I myself saw signals sent from one of the Imperial Beam stations recorded, not only once but three times, at intervals between each record of 1/7th of a second, proving that the signals had made a complete circuit of the world three times, and had recorded themselves on each circular tour. The results obtained on this voyage, especially the effect of daylight on communication, convinced Marconi that it would be advisable to instal a larger plant in the proposed Canadian station than previously contemplated.

CHAPTER IV

TRANSATLANTIC WIRELESS

ON arrival in Canada, after a brief visit to Ottawa to discuss details of the Contract with the Government, Marconi proceeded to Cape Breton Island on the east coast of Canada, to find a suitable site for the Canadian station. Many districts were inspected, including Louisburg, Morien, and Glace Bay : eventually a site was chosen near the town of Glace Bay at Table Head. Marconi then returned to England, leaving me to make the necessary arrangements and construct the station. I was appointed Managing Engineer of the Marconi Company in Canada and remained in Canada for the next six years until 1908. Table Head is in the great coal mining district of Eastern Canada, and the site of the station was actually directly above one of the important mines. The coal mines had attracted workers from every European country and the labour for building the wireless station was a curious mixture. We had Canadians, Indians, Poles, Italians, Americans, and others from south-eastern Europe, all employed at the same time. Marconi had left it to my discretion to determine the size of the buildings, and the details of the plant which would be purchased in Canada, stipulating that the alternator should be of 50 kw. output, instead of 25 kw. as at Poldhu. As it was decided that the station should be built as rapidly as possible I bought a second-hand alternator, but of 75 kw. capacity instead of 50 kw., and a suitable steam engine and boilers. I made the building for housing the wireless plant nearly four times the size of the Poldhu building, which was a fortunate provision since all the extra available room was occupied before we were successful in getting messages across the Atlantic. Meanwhile it had been decided to erect four wooden towers, 210 feet high, both at Glace Bay and Poldhu to support the aerial. The designs of the towers were pre-

34

PLATE VI

VIEW OF FIRST STATION ERECTED IN CANADA IN GLACE BAY, 1902
from which the first wireless transatlantic messages were sent. An early Spring view when the ice from the Gulf of
St. Lawrence packs around the coast

[face p. 34

pared in England and sent out to Glace Bay. They were erected in the form of a square with the building so placed that the aerial insulator leading into the building came exactly in the centre of the square. The aerial as first designed consisted of a square cone upheld by stays stretched between the four towers (see illustration facing this chapter).

While the Glace Bay station was in course of construction Marconi devised a new type of receiver which, until the invention of the Fleming valve, became the standard instrument for reception, superseding the coherer in its different forms. Utilizing the principle, discovered by Professor Rutherford, that electric oscillations, sent through a coil surrounding a fine iron core which had been highly magnetized, had the power of demagnetizing the iron core, Marconi passed an endless band of very fine silk-covered iron wires through a glass tube over which a coil of insulated wire was wound ; through this coil the electric oscillations pass. Over this coil a second coil was wound and connected to a telephone. A pair of horse-shoe permanent magnets were placed, with similar poles together opposite the centre of the coils ; the other poles of these magnets came near the iron band but outside the extreme ends of the glass tube. The band was made in the form of an endless belt and driven slowly round by clockwork. The portion of the band as it approaches the magnet poles becomes magnetized, but owing to hysteresis, as the band moves forward, the magnetized portion of the band is not symmetrically placed with respect to the poles. When an electric oscillation passes through the coil the hysteresis of the iron is removed and the lines of force through the coils are at once changed in number, causing a current to pass through the coil connected to the telephone, and a sound is therefore heard. Marconi found that this instrument, if the setting of the magnets were properly adjusted, was more sensitive, more reliable, and easier to adjust than the coherer.

Meanwhile experiments were continued at Poldhu, better signalling switches were designed, and a new arrangement of the transmitting circuit was tried out. It consisted of single instead of double transformation, in other words only one condenser and one spark gap and jigger were employed. By this means the loss of efficiency when using double transformation was avoided, and the process of tuning the transmitter for different wavelengths much simplified. This system was tried out on many occasions and was the system finally adopted for long range wireless stations at a much later date, but double transformation was reverted to for the experiments which led to the first messages being successfully sent across the Atlantic.

In the summer of 1902 the Italian Government lent Marconi for six months the first-class cruiser *Carlo Alberto* to enable him to carry out a series of long distance tests from Poldhu. Marconi cruised through the North Sea to Kronstad. He also visited Kiel and the coast of Sweden, then down the Portuguese coast to Ferrol and Gibraltar, the north coast of Africa and back to Italy. Everywhere he was able to receive messages by night, but the daylight effect was always in evidence, no signals being received anywhere beyond a distance of about 500 miles during the day.

The construction of the Glace Bay station was completed in October and Marconi left England for Canada aboard the *Carlo Alberto*, arriving at Sydney, Cape Breton, on 31st October. Throughout the whole voyage he was receiving from Poldhu right into Sydney Harbour, but only at night ; after 500 miles from Poldhu no messages were received by day. On 1st November we attempted to receive Poldhu at the Table Head station at Glace Bay but the results were very disappointing, signals being very weak and unintelligible.

The aerials used both at Poldhu and Glace Bay consisted of double inverted cones, there were 50 wires on each side of each cone, 400 wires in all. Many changes were then made in the form of aerial used, but with none of these was any success obtained. Marconi concluded therefore that the power used at Poldhu was insufficient or that the arrangement of plant was not satisfactory. He therefore decided to reverse his experiments, to turn his attention to the transmitting side of the Glace Bay station, and to arrange for Poldhu to receive instead of to transmit, hoping that as Glace Bay had larger power available our signals might get through to Poldhu. A large number of experiments was carried out, with many different arrangements of plant and aerials ; some combinations gave good results, some poor, but an arrangement that gave good results one night, the next night gave very indifferent results, and it thus became difficult to state for certain whether any improvement or progress was being made. In the light of our present-day knowledge it is easy to see where the trouble lay ; we knew nothing then about the effect of the length of the wave transmitted governing the distance over which communication could be effected. We did not even have means or instruments for measuring wavelengths, in fact we did not know accurately what wavelength we were using. Actually we had arranged the aerial and circuits to transmit a wavelength of about 2000 metres, far too short for the distance, and unreliable even as a night wave. Had Marconi originally by an accident arranged the transmitting circuits to emit a wavelength of three or four times the length he actually used the transatlantic communication would have been effected sooner and far more easily, but this might have been a doubtful blessing, because the difficulties experienced led to many investigations, resulting in many developments which otherwise might not have been undertaken.

The first transmitting experiment was started from Glace Bay on 19th November 1902, using a single cone aerial of 200 wires, tuning to a capacity, with the jigger used, of 2/27th mfd., the spark length being 50 mms., but no signals were received at Poldhu. Various changes were made, day by day, and transmission effected every night without success until the 28th, when Poldhu reported signals received for the first time, though they were not readable. The aerial was then changed and only one side, consisting of 50 wires of the cone aerial, was used and a further series of experiments carried out, with practically no results at Poldhu. On 5th December the secondary spark was increased to 100 mm., and for the first time some readable signals were got through. The actual result of this two hours programme was " weak readable signals for first half-hour, nothing doing during the next three-quarters, last three-quarters readable and recordable on tape." This was by far the best result obtained as yet. The next night during the same hours the programme was repeated with exactly the same arrangements but nothing

was received, and again on the following night. It became
evident that the great variation in reception must be due to
extraneous causes, probably variations in the conductive
quality of the medium. It was very difficult to determine
whether one transmitting arrangement was better than another under these constantly varying conditions. Changes
in arrangement were made every day up to the 14th December,
when Poldhu reported " Readable signals through the two
hours programme." This result was much the best as yet
received and, owing to financial pressure and to quiet the
adverse press criticism that was making itself noticeable,
Marconi decided to attempt to send the first message from
Canada the following night using the same arrangement.
Dr. Parkin (later Sir George Parkin, K.C.M.G.) was watching
the experiments, as Correspondent of *The Times,* and the
message he sent addressed to *The Times* was actually the
first message to go by wireless across the Atlantic. It was
transmitted for the first time on 15th December at 1.0 to
3.0 a.m., but conditions were unfavourable and it failed to
get through. It was again sent between 6.0 and 7.0 p.m. with
no better results and repeated during a further programme
from 10.0 p.m. to midnight. On this occasion the result was
excellent " Readable signals throughout " and the first
message had therefore been received on 15th December.
The text of the message was as follows : " *Times* London.
Being present at transmission in Marconi's Canadian Station
have honour send through *Times* inventor's first wireless
transatlantic message of greeting to England and Italy
Parkin." Instructions had however been given to Poldhu
that the message was not to be forwarded to its destination
until further instructions, since Marconi desired that the
Kings of England and Italy should each receive a message
before anyone else.

A message had been received from the Governor-General,
the Earl of Minto, addressed to the King, and this, and one
from Marconi himself, were sent off during the next programme
but again nothing was received. The messages were repeated
on the 17th December but during transmission the alternator
broke down, and repairs were not effected until the evening
of the 18th. Programmes were then continued but, although

parts of the messages were read at Poldhu, it was not until the 20th December that these messages were satisfactorily received. The message for the King of Italy did not however get through until the 21st December. When this had been reported Marconi gave instructions to release the messages, and the fact that wireless communication across the Atlantic had been accomplished was made public. The wording of these three messages is given below :—

" His Majesty the King

May I be permitted by means of first wireless message to congratulate your Majesty on success of Marconi's great invention connecting Canada and England Minto."

" Lord Knollys Buckingham Palace London

Upon occasion of first wireless telegraphic communication across Atlantic Ocean may I be permitted to present by means of this wireless telegram transmitted from Canada to England my respectful homage to His Majesty the King

G. Marconi Glace Bay."

" General Brusati Rome

Occasione prima transmissione radiotelegrafica transatlantica invio conquesto telegramma transmesso altraverso lo Spezio del nuovo al vecchio mondo devotto omaggi a sua maesta il re

Guglielmo Marconi."

Although these three messages were transmitted across the Atlantic and received in England it cannot be said that the wireless circuit was at all satisfactory. There was a great element of uncertainty as to whether any message would reach its destination or not, and so far the cause of this unreliability had not been ascertained. All conditions remaining the same at the two stations, the signals would vary from good readable signals to absolutely nothing and often vary through wide degrees of strength in two or three minutes. This being the case, it was obvious that a large series of experiments would have to be carried out and patient investigation undertaken to ascertain the cause of the unreliability, and find a means of obviating it. From a technical point of view it appeared advisable to refuse to send any more messages, and to devote the time entirely to experimental work, but the publication of the success of the transmission of these messages had attracted world-wide attention to Marconi's work, and it was thought impolitic therefore not to continue to send messages dribbling through. The nights were therefore spent in sending messages and the days in trying out various modifications of circuits or apparatus. During the period from the transmission of the first message on 15th December up to 20th January thirty-eight messages were sent with varying results, some were repeated twenty-four times before they were received, whereas others were repeated six times and received correctly on each occasion. It may be of interest to give the text of one of these messages, since it was the first message sent not of a congratulatory character, and because of an amusing incident in its reception. The message read :—

> " *Times* London by transatlantic wireless Please insert in birth column Jan 3rd wife of R. N. Vyvyan Chief Engineer Marconi's Canadian Station of a daughter Marconi."

This message was received on tape, but atmospherics were present and one atmospheric converted the Jan into Jane, so the telegram as received read " Jane 3rd wife of " etc. On 14th January Marconi left for Cape Cod. This station was now completed and tests were begun between Glace Bay and Cape Cod, but communication could not be effected during daylight. At night, however, Cape Cod signals came through well. On 18th January Cape Cod sent a message to Glace Bay with instructions to reforward it to Poldhu. The telegram was to the King from President Roosevelt. The actual text was as follows :—

> " His Majesty King Edward the Seventh London (by Marconi's transatlantic wireless telegraph)
>
> In taking advantage of the wonderful triumph scientific research and ingenuity which has been achieved in perfecting a system of wireless telegraph I send on behalf of the American people most cordial greetings and good wishes to you and all the people of the British Empire Theodore Roosevelt White House Washington."

This message was sent from Cape Cod from 9.9 to 11.0 p.m. and repeated to Poldhu by Glace Bay from 11.0 p.m. to midnight. It was, however, received direct from Cape Cod by Poldhu from 10.0 p.m. to 11.0 p.m. and was therefore the first message ever received by wireless in England direct from the United States. Further messages were exchanged with Cape Cod until 22nd January, when Marconi left to return to England and the series of experiments were closed down. It was clear that these stations were not nearly in a position to undertake a commercial service ; either more power would have to be used or larger aerials, or both. Marconi deserved the greatest admiration for his courage under his disappointment, and his supreme confidence that he would discover means for overcoming the unexpected difficulties. No further experiments were carried out until 20th March, when programmes with Poldhu were resumed for four nights. Signals were received at Poldhu for two hours each night with complete success, and it was therefore arranged to carry out a limited Press service for *The Times* : the service started on 28th March and continued until 6th April, when the aerial came down due to a silver thaw.

In Canada under certain weather conditions the rain as it falls immediately turns to ice, coating everything with a thick layer of ice. The ice on the aerial quickly became an inch thick and the weight of ice brought down the aerial. We had had no experience previously of this annoying phenomenon but later I arranged means of passing a warming current through the aerial wires to melt off the ice before it became dangerously thick. Such means have since been generally adopted at wireless stations where this ice condition known as a " silver thaw " prevails. The accident to the aerial, and further difficulties, forced us to discontinue *The Times* Press service.

During the whole summer of this year a large series of experiments were carried out between Glace Bay, Poldhu and Cape Cod. Sometimes signals would be received strongly at Poldhu, when Cape Cod, only one-third the distance, could receive nothing. It was conclusive evidence of the variability of the medium through which the waves passed. Meanwhile Marconi continued his investigations in England and came to the conclusion (1) that the aerials hitherto used were too small for the energy put into them, (2) that the distance over which it is possible to signal during daylight increases with the length of wave, that the only efficient way of increasing the wavelength is by increasing the capacity and surface of the aerial more rapidly than the inductance. He found that a small aerial with 1-centimetre spark will give signals at 200 miles range but the range will only be increased to 250 miles with 6-centimetre spark, whereas a large aerial, which will give good signals at 200 miles with a 2-millimetre spark, requires only 4 millimetres to give good signals at 400 miles. As regards daylight range he found that a small aerial required 3-centimetres spark for 400 miles during daylight, while only 5 millimetres was required for the same distance by night. On the other hand a large aerial gave signals of the same strength both by day and night over a distance of 400 miles with only 2-millimetres spark.

He erected a large aerial at Poldhu in the form of an umbrella and sailed on the *Lucania* on the 22nd August to test it out. Marconi had arranged that both Poldhu and Glace Bay should transmit messages throughout the voyage, Poldhu using the new aerial and Glace Bay the single-sided fan aerial. The news sent was published in a daily sheet called the *Cunard Bulletin* and the success of this first ocean newspaper brought about the general publication of newspapers in ocean liners in future.

The distances obtained on the *Lucania* of reception from Poldhu and from Glace Bay were 1000 miles by day and 1700 miles by night. On arrival in New York Marconi instructed me to purchase and erect four 100-feet masts in order to extend the size of the Glace Bay aerial. The new aerial was erected in September. Marconi proceeded to Cape Cod to test the Table Head signals from that station, and on 26th September daylight communication was established with Cape Cod for the first time, but signals were very weak and variable, and only that, when the inductance of the jigger was increased ; with a smaller ratio jigger, 8 to 1, instead of 12 to 1, nothing was received. On Marconi's return to England we continued experiments with Cape Cod and by the insertion of 50 feet of additional inductance in the aerial circuit succeeded in obtaining readable to strong readable signals at Cape Cod during daylight, clearly indicating that the wavelengths hitherto used were not long enough.

In March 1904 a more powerful plant was installed at Glace Bay, the alternator output being doubled to 150 kw. By the end of May the new plant was ready for service. On 7th May Marconi sailed on the *Campania* for New York in order to test out the new transmitting plant installed at Poldhu. The results obtained during the voyage were, however, most disappointing, signals being obtained only 1200 miles by daylight and 1700 miles by night. It was clear therefore that we had to go a long way before a commercial transatlantic service could be inaugurated. It was therefore decided to put the Poldhu and Glace Bay stations to commercial use, and inaugurate a long distance service with ships from these two stations. The Cunard Company signed a contract with the Marconi Company agreeing to pay £10 per 100 words received per ship per day, and this revenue soon became an appreciable one. The long series of experiments had therefore to be closed down ; they had proved that the aerials used were not of sufficient size or capacity, that a still longer wavelength would be required for transatlantic communication, and possibly even greater power. Marconi therefore decided that the Glace Bay station at the Table Head site should be moved, since it was impossible to extend the aerials at the existing site, and I was instructed to find a suitable site inland capable of taking an aerial of a diameter of 3000 feet. Having acquired such a site I was instructed to move the towers and plant to the new site and erect in addition 24 masts in the form of two rings around the four-centre towers, these masts being 180 feet high, with a further ring of 48 poles 50 feet high, so that an aerial 2900 feet in diameter could be erected. I found a site about 6 miles from the original site and about 3½ miles inland. Possession was not, however, obtained until November 1904. The station had therefore to be removed and re-erected in the depth of winter, when the ground was covered with snow and the temperature often below zero. The erection of the station was completed in May 1905 at which date Marconi arrived at the station.

The circular aerial, consisting of 200 wires, had been erected to the second circle of masts and had a diameter of 2020 feet. Having tuned the plant Marconi sailed on the

Campania for England to test it out on the voyage. The results were not as good as hoped for, but the daylight range had been increased to 1800 miles, a gain of 600 miles on the previous best result. In June tests were carried out to Poldhu, and readable signals were recorded at Poldhu at 9.0 a.m. when it was daylight at both stations for the first time, the wavelength used being 3660 metres. An extensive series of experiments were then carried out, using aerials of different sizes, including the extension of the aerial to the third circle of masts but without making satisfactory progress. Meanwhile Marconi continued other experiments in England and discovered that it was possible to transmit more strongly in one direction than in others. He found that if a wire were erected horizontally at a certain height say from east t west, the eastern end of the wire being brought down to the trans-mitter, signals would be received more strongly from the east, and that the aerial became more directive the nearer it was to the ground, the receiving aerial for this directional method being again in an opposite direction, that is from west to east, with the receiver connected to the western end. Marconi decided to try this at Glace Bay and three-quarters of the aerial were therefore lowered, leaving only the segment furthest away from England erected. With this arrangement much better results were obtained. Eventually it was found that with long horizontal aerials it was possible to radiate efficiently waves of any desired length, and this method was eventually generally adopted for long wave long distance communication. Up to this time the wavelengths used were too short for long range communication by daylight, or if a long wave were tried, the aerial was not efficient. It was actually found later that with waves from 7500 to 8000 metres long stronger signals could be obtained by day than by night.

Meanwhile, as it was impossible to extend the aerial system at Poldhu, it was decided to build a new station on the west coast of Ireland. A site was found at Clifden and aerials were erected on the new principle Marconi had discovered. Many new improvements were made in the details of the plant. The type of glass plate condensers hitherto employed was not satisfactory and it was decided to build a large air condenser, composed of metal plates suspended in air separ-

ated by a distance of 12 inches. To obtain the requisite
capacity a very large building was necessary and condensers
on this principle were erected at Clifden and at Glace Bay.
It was also decided to instal at Clifden plant of double the
previous capacity and to increase the capacity of the Glace
Bay plant also to 300 k.w. output. The spark system hitherto
used had not been satisfactory, and Marconi invented an
entirely new method. He had realized that, in order to render
a receiver sensitive only to signals coming from a certain
station, it is necessary to utilize to the utmost the principle
of resonance. In regard to resonance, if waves of a particular
frequency are impinging on the receiving aerial, by how much
can the wavelength be varied or the tuning of the receiver
changed without preventing the signals being received? It
was clear that the narrower this range the more perfect would
be the isolation of the receiver. If the transmitting station
is radiating waves of a certain wavelength, but the damping
of the train of waves can be reduced, the tuning and selectivity
of the receiver will be sharper the less the waves are damped,
and that therefore with continuous waves, or a series of very
slightly damped oscillations, much sharper tuning could be
effected. Marconi realized the shortcomings of the spark
method at present employed, in that it necessarily caused
heavy damping in the train of oscillations, and after careful
study evolved a method of producing practically continuous
oscillations by means of a central disc revolving at a high
speed between two other revolving discs set at a small
distance away from the central disc (see Fig. 11 in the
Appendix). He tried out this arrangement but found that
the continuous oscillations generated were not suitable for
response from the magnetic detector, the type of receiver
then in use. He therefore modified his design of spark discharger to give a series of trains of slightly damped oscillations
instead of continuous waves. With this new arrangement it
was possible to cause his groups of oscillations radiated to
reproduce a musical note in the receiver, distinguishable in
a telephone, and with this arrangement very effective resonance could be effected, moreover the signals, on account of
their particular musical note, could be distinguished in the
receiver from atmospheric noises. The apparatus embodying

this invention is shown in Fig. 12 of the Appendix, and consists of a steel disc, having copper studs firmly fixed at regular intervals near its periphery and placed transversely to its plane. This disc is rotated very rapidly at a peripheral speed of about 600 feet a second, between two side discs of copper, which are made to rotate slowly in a plane at right angles to that of the middle disc. The studs of the central disc are set so as just not to touch the copper side discs. With a suitable frequency and with a potential of 15,000 volts to the condenser, the spark gap is practically closed in the time taken to complete one oscillation, the result being that the primary circuit can continue oscillating without material loss by resistance in the spark gap. The sudden opening of the primary circuit tends immediately to quench any oscillations which may still persist in the condenser circuit, for if the coupling of the condenser circuit is of suitable value, the energy of the primary circuit will have practically all passed to the aerial circuit in the moment of time when the copper stud in the central disc is passing by the copper side discs, but after this the opening of the gap at the discs prevents the energy returning to the condenser from the aerial, and thus the energy is radiated from the aerial in a very slightly damped form, due to the decrement of the aerial itself. Glace Bay and Clifden were both equipped with this new form of disc discharger in 1907. By that date the new condenser had been built, and the new power plant installed, and after satisfactory tests had been effected over several weeks, both by day and night, the Glace Bay and Clifden stations were opened for a limited public telegraph service in October 1907, and an unlimited service at the beginning of February 1908, four years after the first message had been sent across the Atlantic from Glace Bay, and after many difficulties and disappointments. Only those who worked with Marconi throughout these four years can realize the wonderful courage he showed under frequent disappointments, the extraordinary fertility of his mind in inventing new methods to displace others found faulty, and his willingness to work, often for sixteen hours at a time when any interesting development was being tested. At the same time the Directors of the Marconi Company showed wonderful confidence in Marconi, and courage in continuing to vote the large sums necessary from year to year until final success was achieved.

The public service between Clifden and Glace Bay was continued until the autumn of 1909, when it was interrupted by a serious fire at the Glace Bay station, which destroyed the transmitting plant. Profiting by the opportunity new plant was installed, which embodied several interesting engineering features. Instead of using alternators and transformers, high tension direct current was employed for charging the condensers. Special high tension direct current generators were installed to charge a high tension battery of accumulators consisting of 6000 cells connected in series ; the capacity of each cell was 40 ampere hours. The charging and discharging arrangements were suitably arranged to enable different voltages to be obtained. When employing the cells alone a working voltage between 11,000 and 12,000 was available and when working with generators and battery together the voltage could be increased to 15,000. The potential to which the condenser was charged reached 18,000 volts when the battery voltage was only 12,000. This was due to the rise of potential at the condenser plates, brought about by the rush of current through the inductance coils at each charge. No practical difficulty was encountered in regard either to the insulation or maintenance of this very high tension battery. Another improvement was in the design of Disc Dischargers.

On the completion of this installation at Glace Bay the public service between Ireland and Glace Bay was continued and only ceased when the Clifden station was put out of action during the Irish Rebellion. By that date a new station had been erected at Carnarvon in Wales and the service was transferred from Clifden to Carnarvon and continued until the invention of the beam short wave service replaced long wave communication. The Carnarvon high power long wave station has however continued to give useful commercial service. It has still to be relied upon to affect transatlantic communication during those periods when short wave communication across the Atlantic fails on account of magnetic storms, and it is also used for the transmission of pictures and facsimile across the Atlantic.

CHAPTER V

INCIDENTS IN A WIRELESS ENGINEER'S CAREER

DURING the years that elapsed from the start of the construction of the original station at Table Head in Glace Bay until nearly five years later when the Transatlantic Service was opened, there were times when no experiments were being carried out at Glace Bay, while constructional work was in progress at Poldhu or Clifden, and the staff of the station had ample leisure for amusements. Life at Glace Bay was on the whole quite pleasant. The fishing was superlatively good; we had a lake about 100 yards from the site, and a trout brook ran through the site past the house where we lived; there were plenty of brown trout in the lake but when time allowed we used to go to a river about 17 miles away, where the sea trout came in in vast quantities and running to large weights. The river was tidal for about two miles, flowing between two steep and wooded banks, and only about 50 yards wide but very deep. Further up it widened out, and from some of the sand banks in the wider water, when a fresh run of sea trout had just come up, very heavy baskets of fish could be caught. There were salmon too in the river but not many, and they were rarely caught. No more delightful holiday could be imagined than to camp out for two or three days in the early summer on the banks of this glorious but little-known river. Other amusements we had were riding, tennis, canoeing on the lake, and bathing; there was a little shooting though this was poor, except for the duck and wild geese in the late autumn. The winter was trying at times, when the country was covered with snow several feet deep for months on end, but there was always sleighing, skating and ice hockey. The stillness of winter in the country in Canada is extraordinary, when there is no wind. All the birds have left, except a few crows, and although the tracks of countless rabbits are to be seen they

PLATE VII

MARCONI AND HIS STAFF OUTSIDE THE GLACE BAY STATION

The icicles are suspended from an aerial, brought down by a silver thaw

[face p. 48

themselves are invisible. Not a sound can be heard but one's own breathing, beyond the occasional sharp crack of frost in a tree. The winter air is intensely exhilarating and the climate is wonderfully healthy. The people in Glace Bay and Sydney were most kind and hospitable to us, and we were therefore not thrown entirely on our own resources. We had frequent visitors to the station. All important visitors arriving at the Eastern Canadian coast made a point of coming to see the station if they could obtain permission. One of the first of these to come to Table Head was Lord Dundonald, shortly after the South African war. He was received, as the hero of the relief of Ladysmith, with decorated streets ; he spent a day with us. Dr. Parkin, the well-known Imperialist, stayed with us during the first experiments until his message was sent to *The Times*, while on other occasions we had visits from Mr. Fielding, Sir Frederick Borden, Sir Robert Borden, and the Prime Ministers of Nova Scotia and New Brunswick. The British Atlantic fleet visited Sydney near by on several occasions and we saw a good deal of Admiral Douglas and of other officers of the fleet. On one occasion Prince Louis of Battenberg came to the station and while there a telegram came for him ; I remember well his remarking to himself on reading it, " Dear dear, fancy little Ena going to be a Queen." It was the announcement to him of the betrothal of Princess Ena to the King of Spain. We also had visits from officers of the French squadron, and of course saw many officers from the Italian cruiser the *Carlo Alberto*. Reporters were, however, not welcome visitors; they would come without warning and were very difficult to frustrate. We had strict instructions that no interviews were to be granted, but Directors in England had no knowledge of the pertinacity of the American Reporter. I well remember on one occasion the arrival of a reporter from one of the great New York newspapers. He came with a story that Marconi had confessed that he was not the inventor of wireless, but that it had been invented by an officer of the Italian Navy. On my refusing to discuss the matter with him and stating the suggestion was absurd, he stated that he was not going back without a story, and if I did not grant him an interview he would invent one.

On another occasion the Society of American Reporters from the Middle West was touring Eastern Canada and had arranged without permission or notice to visit the station. About 300 suddenly arrived in a special train; I had all doors locked and gave them an impromptu lecture under the aerials. Luckily their time was all mapped out, and after an hour's talk to them, which must have bored them as much as it bored me, they departed. The cuttings describing the visit were sent to me, and one of these, alluding to the lecture I gave them, said "but as the Professor was a Frenchman and spoke very little English we couldn't understand him." On a later date we had a visit from the German fleet. The fleet anchored off Glace Bay, a dangerous roadstead, and the wireless station could be the only object of the visit. In due course the German Admiral and about thirty officers arrived at the gates of the station, where I met them and offered refreshments after their long and hot walk. These were declined and the Admiral stated that they had come to see over the station. I informed him I should be delighted to show them over. Doubtless he had a letter of authority from Marconi or the Directors of the Marconi Company authorizing me to do so. He said he had not; I expressed my regrets that without authority it was impossible for me to admit him. He became very brusque and informed me that His Imperial Majesty would be much annoyed. Again I expressed my regrets and he and his staff went off, again declining any refreshment. The fleet stayed at anchor and I kept a watchman on one of the towers to report. Next day boats put off from the fleet and in due course a crowd of about 150 sailors arrived at the gates. Apparently there were no officers with them: they pushed past me in an unruly mob. I informed them admission was forbidden and if they persisted I would use force to prevent them entering the station. At the time we had a considerable body of workmen employed on certain construction work, and when they saw these men it appeared to strike them there might be trouble. A whistle was blown and they all went out, a disciplined force, and no longer an unruly crowd of men. I was severely attacked in the local papers afterwards for my apparent lack of courtesy. The relations between the Marconi Company and the Germans at that time were not, however, known. It has been mentioned in an earlier chapter that Professor Slaby came to England and was shown by Marconi all his apparatus. Marconi's patents in Germany had been granted, but a year afterwards Professor Slaby took out patents modifying the system used by Marconi somewhat and thus formed a German system, and successfully froze out the Marconi Company from any activity in Germany. As a consequence the Directors of the Marconi Company agreed to discourage visits to any of the stations from Germans, and not to employ them on any of the Marconi stations. At the time when transatlantic communication was established the German Company had not succeeded in effecting any long distance communication, and they were naturally anxious to know how we did it. They tried to obtain information by diplomatic means without success, and it is probable that their visit to Glace Bay was made with the same object. It will not be out of place to mention here an interesting episode which throws light on the attitude of the Germans towards the Marconi Company at that time. On the success of Marconi's experiments across the Atlantic he was invited to Rome, as the guest of the Italian Government. The German Emperor had arrived the previous day, also staying at the Quirinal as a guest of the King. At dinner the night of Marconi's arrival, the German Emperor, after discussing wireless, turned to Marconi and said, " Signor Marconi, you must not think I have any animosity against yourself but the policy of your Company I object to." Marconi replied, " Your Imperial Majesty, I should be overwhelmed if I thought you had any personal animosity against myself but the policy of my Company is dictated by myself."

Since the war those days of bitter rivalry have passed, and with the rapid growth of wireless throughout the world, national companies in different countries, although in active competition in some fields, have learned to cooperate in many directions. German scientists have made many very valuable contributions to the science and technique of wireless, and no one who has had much to do with them can help admiring their thoroughness in all detail, and the very high level of their scientific attainments.

In 1908, after the transatlantic service between Ireland and Canada had been working for nearly a year, I was recalled by Marconi to England for other work. In 1909 I went to South Africa in connection with the proposal to establish a wireless network of communications throughout the Empire; this visit is referred to in a later chapter. Shortly after my return I was sent to Spain to arrange if possible for the transfer of a concession for the coastal and internal wireless communications of Spain, which had been granted to a French Company, who, however, had done very little to carry out the terms of the concession, and I found that this Company was in a very bad financial position. The concession was later taken over by the Marconi Company, much to the surprise and annoyance of the German Company, whose position as wireless contractors to the Spanish Army and Navy at the time was a very strong one. The German Company, when I arrived in Madrid, had nearly completed a powerful transmitting station for the Spanish Army for communication with Morocco and with the chief capitals of Europe. This station was opened by the King of Spain, before the stations that the Marconi Company were constructing were completed. A Spanish National Company was formed, financed by the Marconi Company, to take over and operate the Spanish stations when completed, and one of my duties was to organize a Spanish Staff for this purpose. Under the military regulations at that time in force in Spain, Spanish Military Officers were permitted to take civil appointments. In choosing suitable engineers for the control of the technical side of this new Company one's thoughts naturally turned to those officers of the Royal Engineers of Spain who had had experience of wireless working at the big wireless station built by the Germans for the Army. A certain very efficient officer was selected to take over my position when the stations the Marconi Company were building had been officially approved by the Government as conforming to the conditions laid down in the terms of the concession. The stations which had to be erected were situated around the coast of Spain, at Vigo, Cadiz, Barcelona, and Soller, with a central station near Madrid, capable of communication with all of the coastal stations. Further stations had to be constructed in the Canary Islands, at Teneriffe, and Las Palmas capable of direct communication with Spain. On the completion of these stations a Royal Commission was appointed to inspect the stations, and to ascertain and report whether they conformed in every particular to the conditions laid down. The majority of the members of the Commission had been trained in German wireless methods and were not disposed to pass the stations if they failed in any detail whatsoever to meet the conditions specified. I took the newly appointed Spanish officer, who wore uniform, with me on this tour of inspection, and after visiting the stations in Spain the Commission proceeded to the Canary Islands. The Morocco crisis had just occurred and there was a danger of war with Germany. One day while in Las Palmas the German warship, the *Panther*, anchored there and certain officers came ashore. I was sitting in the window of my hotel overlooking the street and talking to Captain X, when he drew my attention to two men accompanying certain German officers, and pointed out that they were two Telefunken engineers, who had helped to build the military wireless station near Madrid. Naturally we wondered what they were doing on the German warship. As Captain X was well known to them, and as he was in the uniform of the Royal Engineers I asked him to intercept these two Germans, but to be careful to say that he had been transferred for duty in the Canary Islands, and on no account to indicate that he was in any way connected with the Marconi Company. After about an hour's absence he informed me that the *Panther* had in her hold a complete wireless telegraph station which was destined for Agadir and which these engineers were to construct. This was clear evidence that Germany did definitely intend to occupy Agadir, and as the information might be important I cabled it to England on the chance that it might be useful to the Foreign Office. This incident is quoted as an example of the thoroughness of German preparation and of how even in those early days wireless might affect international policy.

Shortly after my return from Canada to England I was appointed the Superintending Engineer of the Marconi Company, and in that capacity was responsible for the design and construction of all wireless stations above a certain size that the Company might erect. I was sent to Russia to inspect the Works and to report on the prospects of the Company exploiting wireless in Russia. As a result of my report this Company was taken over by the Marconi Company, who was extending its interest and influence in wireless communication in every part of the world. The greater part of my time was occupied in designing stations for the suggested Imperial wireless network and for stations to extend the field of transatlantic communication.

CHAPTER VI

CARNARVON AND OTHER WIRELESS STATIONS

THE transatlantic service between Canada and Ireland gradually improved in efficiency, due to modifications in technique introduced into the stations, but the provision of further point to point wireless services was not rapid. Such new links as were constructed in most cases were not competitive with land lines or cables, but filled such gaps where the older methods were difficult to establish or maintain.

This limitation arose from the greater reliability of the metallic connection which, unlike wireless, was not seriously subject to interruption from disturbances arising from natural electrical forces.

It was this interference from " atmospherics " which prevented the application of the already developed technique of mechanical reception of messages at high speeds to a wireless circuit, and so held down the speed of working to that of the human operator. Automatic receivers failed to discriminate between signal and interference, and it was necessary to rely on the human ear to identify the differing characteristics and to reject nature's discords. This process was greatly facilitated by the introduction of the " Disc Discharger " to the stations, by means of which the signals were given a musical note, distinctive from the sound of atmospherics.

Research was largely concentrated on the elimination of the effects of atmospherics. Many circuits and devices of technical promise failed in practical application. The atmospheric is a heavily damped disturbance, that is, it has the nature of a hammer blow and consequently selective tuning is of little avail, since the resonant circuits are all impulsed, by the shock of the atmospheric, at their natural frequency, and a spurious signal results.

The effect of the atmospheric was not confined to the

55

mutilation of the signal, as, if strong, its " crash " was detrimental to the operator's hearing, which had to be sufficiently sensitive to receive a relatively weak signal, and robust enough to withstand the violent noise resulting from the atmospheric. The magnetic detector remained, by reason of its simplicity and robust nature, in general use on ships, but on land was being replaced by the Fleming di-ode valve and by rectifying crystals. Many of the latter were extremely sensitive, but were unstable and liable to be rendered inactive by a strong atmospheric. General Dunwoody discovered that the synthetic crystal " carborundum " not only had good rectifying properties but was also extremely stable, and as a result its use became widespread.

Both the Fleming valve and the crystal were adapted to limit the strength of the atmospheric in the operator's earphones to the strength of the signal. C. S. Franklin produced a valve limiter dependent on saturation, *i.e.* it could be set to prevent the atmospheric from exceeding greatly the strength of the desired signals. In 1911 H. J. Round produced a balanced crystal circuit dependent upon the fact that the carborundum crystal required an impressed voltage to bring it to its most sensitive state. He employed two crystals working in opposition, and so set that one was sensitive to the signal whereas the other only operated when any disturbance exceeded the value to which it had been adjusted ; this had the effect of limiting the maximum signal strength to that value. A considerable improvement in aural reception resulted, not only from the relief given to the operator, but also from the stronger signals given by the improved detector.

To enable wireless to compete between terminals where metallic linking was possible, it was essential that the speed of the wireless link should be at least as rapid as that possible in the metallic circuit.

As already stated, the problem of the atmospheric prevented the direct application of landline terminal technique to wireless reception, and it was necessary to develop recording systems which would allow of discrimination between signal and atmospheric.

One of the earliest types used was the " Telegraphone "—

an instrument comprising a steel wire passing between magnets energized by the signal. This was successfully demonstrated, by the Poulsen Company, on a wireless circuit
between Lyngby in Denmark, and Cullercoats, the transmitters used being Poulsen arcs. Although technically
successful, yet in practical operation there were numerous
disadvantages ; the steel wire on which the message was
recorded magnetically at high speed had to be rewound in
the reverse direction and again run off slowly at a speed
suitable for the operator ; this was cumbersome and gave
rise to delay.

In 1912 a photographic system, due to Franklin, was installed on the Marconi transatlantic service. The signals were
increased in strength by the use of Brown microphone relays
and actuated the string of an Enthoven galvanometer. The
movements of the string were projected by means of an arc
light, and a suitable optical system on to a moving sensitized
tape, which, after exposure, was carried automatically
through developing, fixing, and drying chambers, and was
delivered to the operator in less than three minutes. This
method allowed of visual discrimination between signals and
interference, but was expensive in operation and was soon
superseded by sound recording.

Sound recording gave better discrimination than the photographic method because the characteristic note of the transmitted signal was retained. The signals, magnified as
necessary, were recorded as musical notes on a wax phono-
graphic cylinder running at high speed. When complete the
cylinder was transferred to a reproducing machine, and the
messages were read off at slow speed by an operator. This
system was in vogue for a considerable time as it was cheap
in operation, the wax cylinders being skimmed off to present
a clean surface, and used repeatedly. Speeds up to 180 words
per minute were attained from Wheatstone transmitters
operating Creed high speed high tension switches at the
transmitter.

Duplex Working.—As regards the transatlantic service
between Canada and Ireland, the operation was carried out
on the simplex system until 1913.

The transmitting and receiving aerials were on one site,

and as it was impracticable to use both simultaneously it was the practice for the transmitter to be stopped at intervals and the receiver to be switched in, so that the distant station could acknowledge receipt or ask for any repetitions. As a result the plant was only in use for half the time, and the traffic capacity of the circuit was less than half that which could be achieved by simultaneously working in each direction. In 1913, as a consequence of this restriction, the receiving stations were removed from Clifden and Glace Bay to new sites at Letterfrack and Louisburg, these new sites being about 25 miles from their local transmitting stations. At these new sites two directive aerials were employed, one giving optimum reception from the remote station the other side of the Atlantic, and the other aerial, reception from the local transmitter. On the transatlantic aerial the distant signal was received plus an interfering signal from the local station 25 miles away, while the other aerial received the local station signal only. These aerials were coupled in opposition so that the local signal received in the two aerials was balanced out, leaving the transatlantic signal free from interference. Simultaneous working in both directions was therefore rendered practicable and circuit delays were thus greatly reduced. The application of high speed to duplex working quickly followed.

Early in 1913 the Mercury vapour three-electrode Lieben tube was produced in Germany, and Langmuir in America, and Round in England, developed the three-electrode gas-filled valve with considerable success. These new developments opened up an entirely new field of progress and amplification of signals no longer depended upon mechanical devices. This led to a very rapid development in valve design. Franklin's important patent on reaction in June 1913 marked a considerable advance and by the end of 1913 valves were in general use in the receiving and amplifying circuits on the transatlantic stations.

The progress in the improvement in receiving circuits had been slow but steady ; the duplexing of the circuit by the construction of separate stations had the most marked effect on the improvement of the wireless transatlantic circuit, but the location of the wireless stations on each side of the

Atlantic at the terminals of very long land lines, liable to frequent interruptions, was a serious handicap to the financial and economic success of the wireless circuit in competition with the existing cables.

Meanwhile Marconi was investigating all means of improving long distance communication, and in 1910 with this end in view he installed special receiving apparatus on the S.S. *Princepessa Mafalda,* and himself tested on the voyage to Buenos Aires the distance at which he could receive the signals sent out by the Clifden station. He ascertained that the signals were receivable by day for a distance of 4000 miles and by night for 6735 miles.

As previously stated, from the commercial point of view the transatlantic stations were not well placed ; the Canadian station was at the extreme east of Canada, dependent on a long overhead land line connection to Montreal, and the Clifden station on the west coast of Ireland was equally badly served : furthermore, the great bulk of traffic between Europe and the Western hemisphere was to the United States and not to Canada, and therefore the establishment of a direct service between England and New York gave promise of satisfactory financial returns. The results of these tests of range carried out by Marconi on the *Princepessa Mafalda* proved that it would be possible to establish such a service with a reasonable degree of certainty, and it was therefore decided to build a high power station somewhere in the West of England for communication direct with New York, and that the American Marconi Company, which was controlled by the Parent Company, should build a similar station near New York. It was also arranged that the American Company should construct stations in San Francisco and Honolulu to connect these two important traffic centres. Designs were put in hand and the Engineering Department were busily occupied. A site was selected on the lower slopes of Snowdon, near Carnarvon, and a site for the receiving station at Towyn, further south, on the west coast of Wales.

Developments had taken place in the method of regulation of the spark discharge from the condenser bank. The provision of high tension direct current machines, and a high tension battery, used at Glace Bay and Clifden, was complicated

and required special skill and care in maintenance, and a
new method which had been developed, known as the
" Synchronous Disc Discharger " was adopted for use on
these new stations, by which the disc was directly coupled
to the alternator, and gave out a note equal to twice the
frequency of the alternator. The construction of these new
stations started in 1912.   In September 1912 the Norwegian
Government contracted for a similar station to that being
erected at Carnarvon, to be installed on the west coast of
Norway for direct communication with one of the high power
stations being erected near New York by the American
Marconi Company, and in the same year the British Government entered into a contract for a chain of similar high power
stations for Imperial communications.   Work on this Imperial contract could not proceed however, due to political
considerations, and the contract was not ratified by the House
of Commons until August 1913.

The history of Imperial communications and the various
causes which delayed the erection of the wireless chain in
the British Empire is referred to in a subsequent chapter.
The German Government, however, for a considerable period
before the outbreak of the Great War had been perfecting
a system of wireless communication with distant parts of
the world.   It was realized in Germany that in the event of
war no reliance could be placed on cable communication, and
that without wireless Germany might be isolated telegraphi-
cally from the rest of the world.   Powerful stations were
built in Togoland, in German East and West Africa, and
also in the Pacific Islands owned by Germany.   In the
United States a powerful station was erected by the Company
representing German interests at Sayville, nominally for
communication with German ships at sea, and for the dis-
semination of news.   The wireless central station in Germany
was erected in 1906 at Nauen near Berlin ; the size of this
station was very greatly increased from 15 kw. to about
250 kw. capacity, the mast height was increased from 300
feet to 600 feet, but when the 600-feet mast blew down in
a gale new masts 750 feet high were erected.   Another high
power station was erected in Hanover, using the Goldschm dt
high frequency alternator, and a similar station in America

at Tuckerton, both with masts 820 feet high. At the outbreak of war the British Navy cut every German cable within a few hours, and the foresight of the Germans in preparing in advance a world system of wireless was evident.

Although all the German stations in their colonies were captured or destroyed later in the war, the stations built by or for German interests in America continued to render valuable service to Germany, until finally the United States entered the war on the side of the Allies.

The long wave transatlantic station near Carnarvon, built for direct communication with the United States, embodied at the time of its construction the latest modern knowledge of wireless technique and engineering. From March 1914, when it was first completed, up to the present time, 1932, it has been kept up to date with wireless progress, and many changes in its equipment have taken place, every new or improved type of transmitter has in turn been installed, and it remains the main long wave transmitting station of Imperial and International Communications. This station has been the most important long wave station in England from the time of its completion until the invention of the beam, and the construction of the Post Office extra high power station at Rugby, and is very useful for dealing with traffic when magnetic storms interfere with the short wave beam communication to America. Furthermore, it is extensively used for the transmission of pictures to America and for subsidiary services in European and other countries.

The site of this station is a few miles east of Carnarvon, on a sloping mountain side at Cefn-dhu. The building at the bottom of the aerial is 680 feet above the sea and the aerial, which is erected on masts 400 feet high, slopes gradually up the mountain side, its far end being 700 feet higher up than its lower end. The station was designed to be operated by land lines from the receiving station at Towyn, but later it was found possible to operate direct from London and so to reduce the number of operators required. The power is obtained from the local power supply at 10,000 volts, three-phase alternating current being used. The aerial is of the horizontal directional type, 500 feet in width and supported by masts 400 feet high in rows 900 feet apart.

The original equipment of plant comprised two 300 kw. single-phase alternators direct coupled to 500 horse-power three-phase motors. The synchronous disc discharger was direct coupled to the alternator shaft, and thus driven in synchronism with it. The disc discharger was enclosed in a sound-proof chamber ; above this chamber the condenser bank and transmitting jigger were arranged.

At the receiving station at Towyn the aerial was also of the horizontal directional type, and was supported by five masts in a line on the great circle direction to the American transmitting station. Each mast was 300 feet high and the site was also a mountain site, the last mast of the line being 1400 feet above sea-level. Further, a balancing aerial was erected on poles 80 feet high, at right angles to the main receiving aerial, its purpose being to balance out the effect of the signals from the Carnarvon transmitting station. The station was completed in the spring of 1914 and started testing with Coltano, in Italy, using a wavelength of 5000 metres ; the aerial current was 130 amperes. Programmes with Glace Bay were commenced in April and the wavelength was increased to 11,140 metres. In June 1914 programmes with the similar station at New Brunswick in America were started, and in July New Brunswick started transmission to Towyn. At this time Carnarvon used two wavelengths, the 11,140 metre wave for day communication and the 5800 metre wave for night. By 2nd August the plant was running continuously. The outbreak of war temporarily stopped the tests, but these were resumed at the end of September. The station, however, was used for regular war-time transmission to Russia and Egypt.

Before describing the gradual development in transmitter design up to the modern valve system installed in the Carnarvon station, it may be of interest to describe the course of a message handed in, at that date, at one of the Marconi offices in London for transmission to America. Immediately a message is handed in it is despatched by a pneumatic tube to the instrument room, where it is passed to the punchers, who punch out in Morse code the message on paper tape. This punched tape is passed through an instrument called a Creed transmitter, which transmits the message electrically to the station at Towyn over the landlines. At Towyn the message is reproduced automatically in punched tape, and the tape is then passed through another instrument, called the Wheatstone transmitter, which operates by relays the signalling switches at the Carnarvon station, 60 miles away, and the message is then conveyed across the Atlantic in the form of a stream of closely following electric wave trains, interrupted in accordance with the Morse code, so as to spell out the message, letter by letter. So rapidly and yet so surely does this chain of complicated pieces of apparatus work that the letters are flashed across the Atlantic at the rate of 9 or 10 letters a second or 100 words a minute. These signals are physically represented by the trains of electro-magnetic waves in the ether, each train composed of fifty or more waves 4 or 5 miles in length, built up into trains about 250 miles long, the waves gradually decreasing in amplitude. These pass over the ocean in groups of trains longer or shorter according to whether a dash or a dot has been sent. At the other end the process is reversed. The arriving waves give up their energy to the receiving aerial, and the signals are received aurally by telephone or photographically by galvanometer, or otherwise recorded. In either case they are translated again on to punched tape by means of which they are passed on over the landlines to New York, or other destination, and they are then sent on by messenger or wire to the proper recipient.

This description applies to the methods of handling the transatlantic messages at the time of the inauguration of the circuit from Carnarvon. Many improvements have since been made in eliminating repetitions, reducing the number of operations required, and thus the cost, and in speeding up the handling of the traffic from its reception at the counter to its delivery at its final destination.

Had it not been for the outbreak of war it is probable that a general commercial service with the United States would have been inaugurated before the end of 1914. During the war many improvements were made. Different types of transmitters were tried out, but it was not until March 1920 that a regular commercial service with the United States was instituted by means of the Carnarvon and New Brunswick stations. The war period was used for experimental work, and for a study of the suitability of various wavelengths for this range of communication and much valuable knowledge was thereby acquired.

Previous to and during the war scientists and engineers had been devoting considerable thought to the problem of the production of continuous waves. The advantages of their use were obvious, but the problem of their generation for high power in a satisfactory manner was not an easy one. Poulsen had invented an arc generator of continuous waves, and Alexanderson, Goldschmidt, and Latour, were occupied in designing high frequency alternators. Marconi had already devised a method of producing continuous waves with a plain disc revolving at a high speed between two slowly revolving side discs. He discarded this method for the disc discharger fitted with studs around the rim, whereby he obtained trains of semi-continuous waves, giving a note to the signals in the receiver, the pitch of the note being dependent on the number of studs on the disc, and the speed at which it was caused to revolve. The first discs installed at Carnarvon were on this principle, with the further refinement that the number of studs on the disc corresponded to the number of poles on the alternator, the studs being so set on the disc that the spark passed between the side discs through the studs on the main disc at the peak of each alternation of current in the alternator. Marconi gave further consideration to the problem of producing continuous waves by a spark disc discharger. He considered that, as a synchronous disc discharger produces at constant intervals trains of gradually diminishing oscillations, if a number of such circuits could be provided, each electrically similar, and each discharging through its own disc discharger at definite intervals of time into a common aerial circuit, in such a way that the discharges into the aerial circuit would all be in phase, and so arranged that the discharges from each circuit would overlap into the next circuit, then the equivalent of a continuous wave of constant amplitude would be obtained. He therefore designed a disc, known as the " Timed Disc " based on this idea, which functioned in accordance with his expectations. He used two discs mounted on a common shaft, each with two pairs of electrodes, thus providing four independent primary circuits, and a third smaller disc which was called the Timing Disc, the function of which was to ensure the accurate timing of the main spark discharges by means of a trigger spark.

These new discs were installed at Carnarvon in June 1916 and tests were carried out, with these in circuit, with Coltano in September. Meanwhile the wavelength of the Carnarvon station had been changed to 11,100 metres and the use of two wavelengths, one for day and one for night, was discontinued. The Timed Disc System proved technically a success, but it was very trying on the staff of the station, and in spite of its enclosure in a so-called silence chamber the noise of the discharge was a very objectionable feature ; the accurate setting of the discs and the adjustments of the circuits required considerable skill and experience. At the time of its introduction into the Carnarvon station it was the only form of continuous wave transmitter capable of dealing with a large output to the aerial, and so it fulfilled an important need in commercial communication. It was used for the services from Carnarvon until October 1921. In 1918 the Carnarvon wavelength was changed to 14,000 metres and with the timed disc 220 amperes were obtained in the aerial.

In 1918 Poulsen arc transmitters were installed and used as emergency transmitters giving 100 aerial amperes. On 22nd September 1918 the first message ever transmitted by wireless to Australia was successfully sent from the Carnarvon station, using the " Timed Disc." In 1919 a service with Spain was inaugurated. By February 1920 the aerial current had been increased to 280 amperes, with a wavelength of 14,200 metres. On 1st March 1920 a commercial service with the United States, between Carnarvon and New Brunswick, was opened. Three weeks later the service was extended to duplex and automatic working.

Meanwhile in the United States Dr. Alexanderson had succeeded in producing a satisfactory high frequency alternator and it was decided to instal these in the Carnarvon station. The building was extended to accommodate two of these machines, and they were first used for traffic on 24th April 1921, giving a current to the aerial of 330 amperes.

E

In 1920 the use of the arcs was discontinued and they were dismantled. Meanwhile the aerial was extended further up the mountain. The original aerial was 3600 feet long and this was further extended by another 900 feet. Another improvement was the introduction of what is known as an " Earth screen." This consists of an insulated run of wires supported at about 15 to 20 feet above the ground and covering the ground under the direct influence of the aerial. The width of the earth screen is about 800 feet wider than the aerial and the earth screen extends beyond the end of the aerial. The effect of the earth screen is to reduce the resistance of the aerial circuit substantially, especially when very long waves are used, and so increase the current in the aerial for a given power output.

Developments had been made in the production of transmitting valves and it was thought that the transmitting valve would be the future method of generating high frequency oscillations even for high power stations. It was decided therefore to build a valve transmitter for Carnarvon and this was installed at Carnarvon in 1921. It consisted of thirty large glass valves (M.T.2. type) connected in parallel. By the end of August, after many difficulties had been encountered and surmounted, the valve transmitter was able to give 340 amperes to the aerial with 160 kw. input to the transmitter. Valve tests and demonstrations were continued for the rest of the year, tests being made in transmission to Australia with the valve.

By October 1921 the Timed Disc had become obsolete and was dismantled. The Alexanderson alternators were used continuously for the transatlantic service while the tests with the valve transmitter were in progress, but by September 1922 the valve transmitter was also used for traffic. On 26th March 1923 the operation of the service from the receiving station at Towyn was discontinued, and a direct control from Radio House in London was instituted.

A new valve transmitter, using water-cooled valves, which had just been invented, was installed at Carnarvon at the end of May 1923, and the original valve panel was dismantled. In December the full extension of the aerial, supported by six new 400-foot towers, was available and put into use, giving a current in the full aerial of 560 amperes. In the early part of 1924 the valve panel was increased in power, fifteen water-cooled valves being used. In October the valve panel was put into general use for traffic.

The station was thus provided with two Alexanderson alternators and one water-cooled valve transmitter. It was therefore thought advisable to split the aerial, so that two transmitters could be used simultaneously for different services. This was done and a feeder was run up the mountain side to the upper section of the aerial. The valve transmitter was used on a wavelength of 9500 metres on one aerial, the Alexanderson alternator on 14,000 metres working on the other aerial via the feeder line.

In 1925 an additional aerial was constructed and tuned to 7800 metres and another valve transmitter installed using a power of 40 kilowatts. The wavelength of this transmitter was subsequently altered to 4500 metres and the circuit (GLT) used for traffic to Spain, Egypt and Glace Bay.

This brief record of the changes and extensions at the Carnarvon station indicate the various stages in the progress of long wave transmission, and the development in high power station design that took place from the period shortly before the war, when the synchronous disc discharger was the latest and most effective method of transmission, up to the time when the high power valve transmitter had been successfully introduced. Every type of transmitter had in turn been tried out at Carnarvon ; synchronous disc, timed disc, arc, alternator, glass valve and, finally, water-cooled valve. A great deal of knowledge, based on the experience obtained with the use of these different methods, had been gained and was therefore available for the design of other high power long wave stations, when the discovery of the utility of short waves and the invention of the beam system made it clear that long wave transmission was not likely to be used much in future for new long range circuits, although the stations already built on the long wave principle would still serve important needs. The Carnarvon station remains in service with both the alternator and valve transmitters, and is used by the Traffic Department of Imperial and International Communications Ltd. for helping out services which at times become difficult on the short wave, and for picture transmission.

The development of long wave wireless communication from the early days in 1901 up to the invention of the beam system had been chiefly due to the intensive efforts to establish a satisfactory method of ensuring reliable wireless communication across the Atlantic, and to obtain a share of the heavy and profitable traffic passing between Europe and America.

Mention has already been made of the high power long range wireless station at Nauen, built by the Germans before the war. This station was considerably enlarged and extended and equipped with the German type of high frequency alternators.

In France high power long wave stations were constructed at the Eiffel Tower, Bordeaux and Ste. Assise. At the Eiffel Tower, the famous French wireless expert, General Ferrie, had built the station underground, so as not to interfere with the aesthetic appearance of the Champ de Mars, and the Eiffel Tower was used to support the aerial. The transmitter was of the spark system until recent years and the spark was given a musical note of 2000 frequency, the rotating spark discharger being coupled to a 150 kw. 1000 cycle alternator.

The Bordeaux station was erected during the war by the United States Navy for communication between France and the United States, for special war services. It was completed in 1920 and from that date has been used for commercial services.

The Ste. Assise station was designed to be the main radio centre of French communications. The construction of this station was started in January 1921. Ste. Assise is situated about 25 miles from Paris and is a fine example of a modern long wave transmitting station. It was divided into three sections, devoted respectively to long range overseas communications, European continental routes, and special duplex services to London and Madrid. The long wave system installed is the Latour high frequency alternator and the main aerial system is supported by a number of masts 800 feet high.

There were, of course, many other wireless stations erected in the different countries in Europe, and in other parts of the world, but the most important, and the most typical, up to the end of the Great War were those to which reference has been made.

CHAPTER VII

HISTORY OF IMPERIAL WIRELESS COMMUNICATIONS

A S a result of the experience gained in the working of the transatlantic service I was convinced that it would be practicable to establish a chain of wireless stations throughout the British Empire, and I wrote an article advocating " Imperial Wireless Communications," which appeared in *The Times* shortly after my return to England at the end of 1908. The scheme advocated attracted a considerable amount of support, and the then Prime Minister, Mr. Asquith, shortly after the publication, in a speech on Empire problems, alluded to the possibility of Imperial Wireless communication. There was not much engineering work on hand in the Company at the time and its financial position was very difficult. I therefore obtained Marconi's consent to my visiting South Africa to endeavour to interest the South African Government in the suggested Imperial Wireless scheme. His consent was only granted on condition that I went at my own expense, with the proviso that if I succeeded in getting any orders while in South Africa my expenses would be paid. South Africa was a virgin field for wireless, and I was fortunate in obtaining orders for two coastal stations. On arrival I found that the *Times* article had been reproduced in the South African press, and my mission was therefore simplified. I saw General Botha and General Smuts, and in explaining the proposal for Imperial Wireless Communication with South Africa emphasized what I thought were the economic advantages. Well do I remember General Smuts replying to me, " That's all very well, but what appeals to us more particularly is that it will draw more closely the bonds of Empire," with which sentiment General Botha concurred. I did not think they really meant it, and had accepted the ideal of Imperial unity so wholeheartedly as the words indicated, and their future careers so amply proved, nor could

PLATE VIII

BEAM AERIALS AT DORCHESTER WIRELESS STATION

[face p. 70

anyone at the time have realized what magnificent services were to be rendered to the Empire both in the Council Chamber and in the Field by these great men.

In 1910 Mr. G. C. Isaacs was appointed Managing Director of the Marconi Company and took up the proposal for Imperial Wireless Communication with great vigour. Many discussions were held with the different authorities, and in certain directions considerable opposition was encountered. Rival systems were advocated, and the suggestion that the communications should be effected by private enterprise was opposed. In May 1911 the Imperial Conference approved the proposal that an Imperial Wireless Telegraph system should be erected, and after protracted negotiations, over a year later, in July 1912, the British Government entered into a contract with the Marconi Company for the chain of Imperial Wireless stations, but when the contract was submitted to the House of Commons for ratification, several members threw doubt as to whether the Marconi system was the best and other objections to the contract were raised, so it was referred to a Select Committee to report thereon. In January 1913 the Postmaster-General, Mr. Herbert Samuel, in order to meet the vociferous criticism as to the merits of the Marconi system in comparison with the German and other foreign systems, none of which had established long-distance commercial communication at that date, appointed a Committee, presided over by Lord Parker of Waddington, " To consider and report on the merits of the existing systems of long-distance wireless telegraphy and in particular as to their capacity for continuous communication for the distances required by the Imperial Chain." The Committee issued their report in April, after inspecting the various systems that were in existence, and stated, " The Marconi system is at present the only system of which it can be said with any certainty that it is capable of fulfilling the requirements of the Imperial Chain." The Committee also reported that " the only high frequency generator we have yet seen tried with success over long distances is the Marconi continuous high frequency machine." On 2nd July the Select Committee decided not to pursue their enquiries further and on 4th July Mr. Samuel made a statement in the House of Commons regarding a new contract with the Marconi Company for the "Imperial Wireless Chain." The revised contract was debated in the House on 8th August 1913 and ratified.

The main terms of the contract provided that the Marconi Company would construct stations, under stringent guarantees as to hours of communication, efficiency of service and speed of working, in England, Egypt, East Africa, South Africa, India and Singapore, the stations to be the property of the State and the price to be paid for each station to be £60,000. The Marconi Company during a period not exceeding twenty-eight years to receive 10 per cent of the gross receipts by way of royalty in respect of the earnings at each station : many restrictions and safeguarding clauses were inserted. The technical specification attached to the contract provided for what was then the most modern method, the synchronous disc discharger, in which the disc is directly coupled to the alternator and provided with studs corresponding to the number of alternator poles, so that the moment of discharge between the side discs and studs of the main disc takes place at the peak of each alternator cycle. The specification covered the provision of every detail of the plant, from the power plant to aerial and also with regard to the buildings.

On the ratification of the contract, the responsibility of carrying it out was entrusted to the Author, and technical conferences regularly took place with the Engineering Department of the Post Office. Sites were selected and approved, at Leafield and Devizes in England, in Egypt and in India. Engineers were sent to mark out the sites and supervise the construction of the stations. By the summer of 1914 these sites were in the possession of the Company. Constructional work was in progress, and the erection of the masts was under way, when war broke out and the whole situation changed. The mast system erected at Leafield was used as an intercepting receiving station for enemy signals, and a temporary station was rushed up in Egypt for strategic communication with England on the site of the Imperial station, in view of the possibility of the cables being cut. At the end of the year the Post Office cancelled the Contract. In due course the Company took action against the Post Office for the breaking of the Contract and was awarded nearly £600,000 damages.

After the war, in 1919, the Marconi Company put forward a very ambitious scheme for a new Imperial Wireless network, including not only the main trunk routes of the British Empire, but embracing a large number of feeder and subsidiary stations. Another Imperial Wireless Telegraphy Committee was appointed by the Government to consider what high power stations it was desirable, on commercial and strategic grounds, to construct and to prepare estimates of the capital and annual costs of each station. The Committee was under the Chairmanship of Sir Henry Norman and the Committee reported at very considerable length at the end of May 1920. In their report they criticized adversely the proposal of the Marconi Company, chiefly on account of its comprehensiveness and that it would confer a monopoly on the Company. The main recommendations were :—

1. That a scheme of Imperial Wireless communications be established connecting the communities of the Empire by geographical steps of about 2000 miles.

2. That the wireless system employed be that involving the generation of radiotelegraphic energy by thermionic valves.

3. That the service of communication between Leafield and Cairo by Poulsen arc, shortly to be in operation by the Post Office, be the first link in the chain of communication with the British communities in Africa and that this communication be continued by a valve station near Nairobi in East Africa, and by the alteration of the ex-German station at Windhuk to a valve station to complete the connection with East Africa.

4. That for communication with India, the Far East, and Australia, valve stations be erected in England, near Cairo, at Poona (or other Indian station), at Singapore, at Hong Kong, and in Australia at Port Darwin or Perth.

5. That similar communication be established by valve stations between England and Canada.

6. That the construction of the stations be entrusted to the
   Engineering Department of the Post Office and the
   corresponding Dominion and Indian Authorities.

The report was a very bitter attack on private enterprise,
and in several of its recommendations it went contrary to the
advice of previous commissions. The recommendations, however, were not accepted.

Meanwhile the Post Office had installed a Poulsen Arc at
the Leafield station, the English transmitting station of the
original Imperial contract, and had likewise installed a
Poulsen Arc at the Cairo station, which had been built by the
Marconi Company as an emergency station during the war.
In 1921 these stations were opened but the service they gave
in the light of modern communications was very indifferent.

Another Imperial Conference was held in 1921, at which
it was agreed that the chain of Imperial stations should be
pushed forward as rapidly as possible. The Marconi Company
continued negotiations with the Government regarding the
establishment of the Chain of stations, but questions of State
versus private ownership were not settled, and no decision
was definitely come to until 1924, except that the English
end of the Chain should be owned and operated by the Post
Office. In 1923 the Post Office acquired a large site near
Rugby and proceeded to erect a very high power station for
Imperial long wave communication. Meanwhile the Marconi
Company made a tender which was accepted, for the
erection of a transmitting station in Australia of a power of
1000 kilowatts and with an aerial supported by twenty masts
800 feet high. In South Africa a Company was registered for
erecting and operating a station for Imperial communication.

In February 1923 the Government appointed yet another
Committee to report on the whole subject of the Imperial
Wireless Scheme, and their recommendations were that the
Post Office should own and operate directly all wireless
stations for communication with the various parts of the
Empire, but that the business organization of the Post Office
for effecting this should be improved. This proposal could
not have been accepted in its entirety however since the
South African Company had already received a concession

from the South African Government, and a high power station was already in course of construction for service with England. In 1924 the Beam system was invented and all previous schemes were nullified by this great development. The Marconi Company opened negotiations with the Government with the view to the Beam system being utilized for the Imperial chain, with the result that, in July 1924, an agreement was concluded between the Postmaster-General and the Company for the construction of stations on the Beam system capable of communicating with Canada, India, South Africa and Australia. The main features of the contract were :—

That the Company erect transmitting and receiving stations on sites provided by the Government capable of working simultaneously, the transmitting station to have an input power of at least 20 kilowatts with an aerial system so designed as to concentrate the emitted waves within an angle of 30 degrees. The receiving station to have a similar system, designed to focus the received waves, and the stations to be capable of operation from the Central Telegraph Office in London by remote control.

That the Company undertakes to have similar stations erected in Canada, South Africa, India and Australia.

That the stations shall be capable of communication at a speed of 100 words per minute in each direction exclusive of any repetition to ensure accuracy

in the case of Canada for a daily average of 18 hours
,,   ,,   South Africa   ,,   ,,   ,, 11 hours
,,   ,,   India   ,,   ,,   ,, 12 hours
,,   ,,   Australia   ,,   ,,   ,, 7 hours

That the Company shall receive the actual cost of the stations plus 10 per cent profit, subject to the maximum cost of each station not exceeding a certain figure laid down in the contract, and that the Post Office will pay a royalty of $6\frac{1}{4}$ per cent of the gross receipts of the Beam stations so long as any Marconi patents essential for the working of the stations are contained therein.

Many severe technical conditions were laid down as to tests and guarantees. The Company accepted the contract, knowing that the actual cost would largely exceed the maximum payment they could receive for capital cost, but realizing that refusal of acceptance would entail very serious consequences to the prestige and financial future of the Company.

The publication of the Agreement led to developments in the Dominions with the view to the Beam system being tried. In South Africa the Marconi Company was erecting a high power long wave station for the South African Company, and had already erected four masts 800 feet high, when the possibility of short wave beam communication seemed to offer a better solution. Work was therefore suspended on the long wave station and the Wireless Telegraph Company of South Africa contracted with the Marconi Company for the erection of a beam station for direct communication with England.

The Amalgamated Wireless Company of Australia made a similar contract. In Canada the Canadian Company started the erection of similar beam stations under the supervision of Marconi engineers. In India an Indian Communication Company was formed, and the Marconi Company likewise received a similar contract. For its own telegraph services, to New York and to South America, the Marconi Company decided to erect beam stations, and further beam stations were decided upon to fulfil the terms of a concession that the Marconi Company had received from the Portuguese Government to connect up Lisbon with Cape Verde Islands, Brazil, Portuguese West Africa, and Portuguese East Africa.

At last, after sixteen years of hopes and disappointments, an Imperial Wireless Chain of Communications was actually under construction and I had the personal satisfaction of being responsible for the construction of these stations and their engineering design. Mr. C. S. Franklin himself designed the beam aerials, and the actual transmitters used, and it was due to his careful attention to detail, and profound technical knowledge and experience on short wave working, that the stations when erected were successful from the start and fulfilled the very severe guarantees that they were called upon to perform.

The sixteen years delay in establishing an Imperial Wireless Chain had however been a blessing in disguise, not only to the Empire but also the Marconi Company. The procrastina-

tions, criticisms, opposition and political considerations, responsible for the delay, which were many times most irritating
and disheartening, continued until a day arrived when a new
method became available, profoundly changing the whole
technique of long distance wireless communication. Had
the State built wireless stations on the long wave principle
their performance would have been indifferent as compared
with what can be done with short wave beam communication,
whereas had the Marconi Company been permitted to build
and operate them on its own account, all the money so ex-
pended would have had to be written off. It might further be
said that the incentive to develop a system working on short
waves would not have had the same force, and that the long
delays in coming to a final decision had therefore a beneficial
effect on wireless research and invention.

CHAPTER VIII

HISTORY OF BEAM DEVELOPMENT

THE proposal, put forward in 1924 by the Marconi Company to the Government, that the Company was prepared to guarantee a satisfactory high speed commercial service to all parts of the British Empire by short waves, concentrated in one direction in the form of a beam, in place of all previously considered proposals embodying the use of long waves, was of so sensational a character, and the advantages offered were of so sweeping a nature, that the Government, after careful investigation, accepted the offer under strict guarantees and penalties. Much technical criticism was directed upon the proposal, but the success of the stations when erected changed the whole technique of wireless communication throughout the world. It is therefore of interest to trace the steps which led to this revolution in wireless telegraphy.

In his very earliest experiments, Marconi had demonstrated that short waves could be directed in a beam and, using a parabolic reflector, he gave Sir William Preece a demonstration of this in 1896. From this early date until 1916 no further research on the possibility of short wave communication was carried out. The field did not appear a promising one ; it was known that the attenuation of short waves was very high, and the power that could be used with short waves was at that time very small. Nothing was known of the effect of the Heaviside layer in the upper atmosphere, nor of its peculiar properties of being able to reflect waves, and consequently research on short wave propagation was entirely neglected. Marconi pointed this out in 1922 in a paper he read to a joint meeting of the American Institution of Electrical Engineers and the Institute of Radio Engineers ; and explained that during the war, early in 1916, he decided to investigate the subject of short wave propagation, with

PLATE IX

C. S. FRANKLIN

[face p. 78

the idea of using beams of reflected waves for certain war purposes, as he was impressed with the advantages which such a system would afford in minimizing interception by the enemy. He further stated that he could not help feeling that, by confining all experimental work to long waves, research workers had perhaps got into a rut, and that further investigation of short wave phenomena was likely to develop in many unexpected directions, and open up new fields of profitable research.

In his first tests in 1916 Marconi used a coupled spark transmitter and a crystal receiver. The reflectors employed were made of a number of wires, tuned to the wave used, and arranged on a cylindrical parabolic curve with the aerial in the focal line. Reflectors with apertures up to $3\frac{1}{2}$ wavelengths were tested, and the measured polar curves agreed with the calculated values. With this apparatus, using a wavelength of three metres, good communication was obtained up to a distance of six miles. The investigation appeared to be so important that Marconi arranged that Mr. C. S. Franklin should devote his attention to a study of the problem of short wave propagation, and tests were continued in England. In 1917, using a wavelength of 3 metres a range of 20 miles was obtained from Carnarvon, with a reflector at the transmitting end only. In 1919 Franklin succeeded in using thermionic valves for the generation of very short waves. Up to his investigation of the problem the standard transmitting valves as used on long wave stations developed trouble at the seals when used for short wave generation. During further tests and utilizing a wavelength of 15 metres, clear and strong speech was received at Kingston Harbour, 78 miles from Carnarvon. Experimental stations were then set up at Hendon and near Birmingham, a land range of 97 miles, and using 700 watts input, the speech received was of good quality. The great value of the reflector was demonstrated by careful measurements, which showed that when reflectors were used with the aerials at both transmitting and receiving ends the value of the energy received was 200 times greater than obtainable without reflectors.

Marconi therefore decided to carry out experiments on a larger scale. A short wave transmitter of 12 kilowatts input was erected at Poldhu and a parabolic reflector was built, supported by masts 325 feet high, so that wavelengths could be tried from 97 metres downwards.

As the receiving station Marconi's yacht the *Elettra* was used, so that field strengths could be measured at varying distances up to the maximum practicable, and also across the width of the beam. No receiving reflector could of course be used on the yacht, and it could be relied upon therefore that, whatever ranges and strength of signal were obtained, they would be much improved in the case where a fixed receiving station with a suitable reflector was erected.

Up to the time of the Poldhu-*Elettra* experiments all previous long distance tests on wavelengths of 200 metres and less had been carried out during the hours of darkness and on small power. The general opinion of experimenters in this field had been that the range of communication with short waves during the day was extremely variable and short, that the night range was exceedingly variable and freaky, and too unreliable to trust to for commercial work, furthermore any considerable amount of intervening land seriously reduces the distance at which it is possible to communicate. The *Elettra* experiments showed the fallacy of these conclusions. After a series of tests in the Mediterranean off the south coast of Spain with consistently good results at night, although by daylight signals weakened (on the wavelength then used, namely, 97 metres) according to the distance and to the altitude of the sun, Marconi decided to proceed into the South Atlantic to ascertain the extreme ranges of communication : he sailed as far as St. Vincent, and found that signals could be received up to 1250 nautical miles from Poldhu by daylight, but by night the signals were always of astonishing strength up to the limit of the distance of his voyage, 2230 nautical miles. Signals could be received at night with the low frequency amplifier switched off, and Mr. Mathieu, who was on the *Elettra*, estimated the strength of the night signals as between 400 and 500 microvolts per metre in the aerial, and with such a strength no trouble whatever was experienced from atmospherics.

The signals were far stronger than those received on the long wave from either the Post Office station at Leafield, or the high power long wave station at Carnarvon, even when the power of the transmitter at Poldhu was reduced to 1 kilowatt.

The results were so encouraging that Marconi felt confident he had a new system which would probably replace the existing long wave system for long range communication; he therefore decided to return to England and make a series of extensive investigations. The Poldhu short wave transmitter was increased in power to 20 kilowatts input, and in February 1924 further tests were carried out covering the greatest distances on the earth. A receiver was installed on the S.S. *Cedric* and reception tests were carried out by Mr. Mathieu on the voyage to and from New York. Poldhu used no reflector during this test, transmitting on a wavelength of 92 metres. The Poldhu transmitter was giving a radiation from the aerial of about 17 kilowatts. Using this wavelength the daylight range was found to be 1400 nautical miles, and it was confirmed that the signal intensity is proportional to the mean altitude of the sun at all times. Signals of great intensity were received in New York by night. During these tests the Australian Company were listening in, and reported that the signals were received in Sydney, Australia, quite clearly and of good strength from 5 to 9 p.m. Greenwich mean time and also from 6.30 to 8.30 a.m. In Canada it was possible to receive the signals for about 16 hours out of the 24. The results were so impressive that Marconi decided to attempt to telephone to Australia, still using the 92-metre wavelength and no reflector, with the result that good speech was successfully transmitted to Australia from England for the first time on the 30th May 1924.

It must be remembered that these later tests had all perforce been carried out without the use of reflectors at either end, and Marconi was convinced by the results obtained that, given adequate reflectors at both ends, not only would the strength of signals be much greater but also a reduction of any interference by atmospherics or other causes would be effected. Meanwhile Franklin, who had been devoting his whole time to the study of short wave transmitting problems, had been giving particular attention to the design of efficient reflectors. The reflector used at Poldhu was of the parabolic

F

cylindrical type composed of a number of wires separated by about ⅛th of a wavelength apart, and the focal length of the parabola was made equal to either ¼ or ¾ of the wavelength, the aerial wire being placed at the focus. It had been found that the reflector should be as large as possible, compared with the wavelength, and that the reflector wires gave the best results when made up of a series of wires insulated from each other and each equal to one-half a wavelength. The divergence of the beam was a function of the aperture of the reflector in terms of wavelength. To obtain a 10-degree beam on a 100 metres wavelength with a parabolic reflector involved therefore a costly structure. Franklin, realizing this, endeavoured to obtain a narrow beam of radiation by other methods. He came to the conclusion that it would be possible to get the same, or even better concentration of radiation in a narrow beam by the employment of two grids parallel to each other, one grid constituting the reflector, and the other grid forming a series of multiple aerial wires, energized simultaneously from the transmitter at a number of feeding points, so as to ensure that the phase of the oscillations in all the wires is the same. He was satisfied by calculations, which were afterwards confirmed by measurements, that given such an arrangement the directional effect would be a function of its dimensions relative to the wavelength employed. He also considered the possibility of restricting the radiation in the vertical as well as the horizontal plane, and thought that by arranging the vertical components of the aerial wires into half-wave units, one above the other, when brought into phase he would create such an effect to a certain degree. Such an aerial was constructed and fulfilled Franklin's predictions, and after modifications in detail, is the aerial used in all the beam stations and forms the basis upon which competing organizations have designed their aerial systems, modified in different ways, in order to avoid using the Franklin patents.

In the previous chapter it was stated that in July 1924 a contract was made with the Post Office for Imperial Wireless communications by means of the new short wave beam system. The remarkable results obtained during the Poldhu-*Elettra* tests, and the successful reception in Australia and

Canada of the short wave signals, had convinced Marconi and his assistants of the practicability of the scheme, and due to political and commercial considerations the Marconi Company found itself in a position where it was essential to take enormous risks and give guarantees of performance for the effective working of a new system that had as yet never been used on any commercial circuit. No grid aerial on Franklin's proposal had as yet been erected. Very little was known as to the behaviour of short waves other than 90 or 100 metres except over very short distances, and no plans or designs had been prepared for any commercial short wave station.

Marconi and the Marconi Company, with the knowledge of the remarkable results obtained, were however full of confidence that they could fulfil the arduous conditions, but the British Post Office could not be expected to be so optimistic, and the construction of the extra high power long wave station at Rugby was proceeded with. The writer was entrusted with the carrying out of the Imperial Contract and, in the closest touch with Marconi and Franklin, plans of the buildings, machinery, towers, aerial and feeders were prepared, sites selected and the work of construction was started. An intense concentration was at once made on the study of short wave propagation. A new series of tests were inaugurated between Poldhu and Marconi's yacht the *Elettra*, with the object if possible of overcoming the limitation of the hours of working brought about by the effect of daylight, by the employment of still shorter waves. Tests were therefore carried out over varying distances with four wavelengths, 92, 60, 47 and 32 metres respectively, and it was found that over long distances the daylight range for communication steadily increased as the wavelength was reduced, the 32-metre wave being received all day off the coast of Syria at a distance of 2100 miles, whereas the 92-metre wave was not effective during the day at this distance, and its range appeared to be limited to 1000 miles by day. The 60-metre wave was better than the 92-metre and the 47-metre still better. It was naturally assumed that wavelengths still shorter than 32 metres would be even more effective. The results of these tests raised the scientific question as to how they travel round the earth. It was clear that the results could not be explained by refraction, as the signals received over these great distances were many thousand times stronger than could be possible if due to refraction only. The theory was advanced, and is now generally accepted, that the waves are reflected from the conducting layer of ionized gases in the rarified upper atmosphere, known as the Heaviside layer, and the fact that longer waves travel best by night, and the shorter by day, conforms to the theory of the deeper ionization of the upper atmosphere by the sun during hours of daylight.

In October 1924 tests were carried out on a wavelength of 32 metres with Montreal, New York, Rio, Buenos Aires, and Sydney, Australia, and it was found possible to receive messages, when using less than 12 kilowatts at the Poldhu transmitter in New York, Rio and Buenos Aires, even when the whole of the track between Poldhu and these cities was in full daylight. The Australian tests showed that with this wavelength, at that date, it was possible to communicate for 23½ hours out of the 24. These tests were carried out without the use of reflectors at either end ; their object was to ascertain the best wavelength to utilize for the various distances, and the results obtained determined the decision as to the size and form of the aerials to be erected on the mast already in process of construction at the Imperial beam stations.

It had already been proved that the directional effect of a reflector is a function of its dimensions in relation to the wavelength employed. Hence it followed that by the use of still shorter waves than what were contemplated when the Imperial Beam Contract was made, an aerial could be erected on the mast system constructed giving a much greater concentration than the 30 degrees specified in the contract. Actually the concentration was increased to nearly three times the figure called for.

The employment of the *Elettra* for the important experiments, which demonstrated the practicability of short wave working over long distances, reduced the period of preliminary research very substantially. A moving station for purposes of observation and measurement possesses great advantages over a fixed station where problems of range, directional effects, and other propagation questions require solution. The *Elettra* was able to sail across the path of the beam to ascertain if the signals from Poldhu still travelled in the form of a beam at great distances, and also to measure the intensity of the strength of signals both by night and day over varying distances and with different wavelengths. Many months' investigation were undoubtedly saved by the use of Marconi's yacht for this purpose.

The observations made during these experiments enabled the wavelengths for the various communications required at the Imperial Beam stations to be fixed. Sites had been chosen in agreement with the engineers of the Post Office, at Bodmin in Cornwall for transmitting to Canada and South Africa, and near Bridgwater for the corresponding beam receiving station for reception from Canada and South Africa. For transmitting to India and Australia a site was selected near Grimsby, with the corresponding receiving site near Skegness.

Another site was selected at Dorchester for transmission to New York, Buenos Aires and Rio, with a corresponding receiving site at Somerton. Constructional work was put in hand at each site and also at the corresponding stations in the distant countries.

The design of the short wave transmitter had yet to be made and Franklin took up this problem himself. It has already been mentioned that the standard type of transmitting valve which was satisfactory for long wave transmission developed trouble at the seals with the very high frequencies used, which cause very large currents to pass into the grid and anode. The production of a satisfactory power valve for short wave working was a difficult problem at the time, not only on account of the necessity of much larger seals to the valves, but also due to the extreme dissimilarity in behaviour of apparently identical valves. This trouble was eventually traced to losses in the deposits on the glass, owing to high frequency induced currents, and means were found to counteract the effect. A power valve was eventually designed with a copper anode, cooled by oil circulation instead of water, which could deal with 10 kilowatts input to the anode. The final design of the short wave transmitter employed two of these valves in a bridge circuit in the power amplifier, arranged so that the valve capacities were balanced out. The design of the transmitter was made as flexible as possible, since the wavelengths chosen for each communication might have to be changed. The two valves in the power amplifier connected in " push-pull " were capable of working at 20 kilowatts input. The constancy of wavelength was provided by a valve drive taking less than 100 watts, and the power from the drive was amplified by three successive stages. The transmitter was originally designed to be adjustable to any wavelength from 60 metres to 20 metres, but after further experience the design of the transmitter was altered to cover a range of from 40 metres to 15 metres. To economize frequencies the method of wave change keying for signalling as used at Poldhu was abandoned, and what is known as absorber keying, whereby the aerial only radiates when the signal is transmitted, eliminated the employment of a spacing wave. The power amplifier was made in a single panel, another panel comprised the circuits and valves for absorbing during the spaces between signals, and a third panel included the drive and the first two stages of amplification. This panel was provided in duplicate in all cases where a different wavelength had to be used for day and for night communication. It was possible by this arrangement to change over from the day to the night wave, and vice versa, in about ten minutes. The problem of the best method of reception of the short wave signals had also to be solved. The design of the form of commercial receiver to be used on the beam station was entrusted by Marconi to Mr. Mathieu, who had assisted him on all his short wave receiving tests on the *Elettra*. Mr. Mathieu realized that he could rely on the large amplifying factor of the beam receiving aerial, which would ensure that the signal strength passed to the high frequency stage of the receiver was already of a high amplitude, and he therefore wisely at the time decided to design the receiver with only one stage of high frequency amplification, and to rely on low frequency amplification for such further stages as might be necessary. He also realized the possibility that the constancy of the transmitted wavelength might vary somewhat from time to time, due to drift according to the temperature of the air in the transmitting room and other causes. He therefore designed the receiver to respond to the wavelength transmitted with a possible variation up to 10,000 cycles, so that if a variation in frequency within such limits did take place the receiver would still be responsive without adjustment. It was known that the strength of the signals, reflected from the upper atmosphere, varied greatly from moment to moment, but it was also thought that the high amplifying factor of the beam aerial would provide sufficient strength of signal with a suitable design of receiver to ensure recordability of the signals even when the signals were at their minimum value. At their maximum value the strength of signals might be a disadvantage, so limiting circuits were introduced in the receiver to reduce the peak strength of the received signals. The design of receiver produced by Mr. Mathieu was sound in conception, and fully satisfied the needs of the commercial services when these were inaugurated. It must be remembered that both in the case of the transmitter and receiver design the research staff were dealing with entirely new problems, and it is remarkable that with no precedents to help them, with only the observations they had made on the results obtained in experimental research, they were able to design apparatus which met the severe requirements of a particularly rigid contract, demanding reliability and a high degree of technical performance to fulfil conditions of continuous commercial communication.

Years have passed now since these designs were produced and much further experience gained, and knowledge gleaned. The modern design of transmitter has resulted in considerable modifications in the original beam transmitter as designed by Franklin and the same applies as regards the development of modern receivers. Critics, with the information now available of the working of these circuits over a number of years, may ask why such and such was not embodied in the designs, but those who can carry their minds back to the utter lack of knowledge which existed regarding short wave communication at the time when the beam stations were constructed must admire the very high degree of foresight shown by those two engineers responsible for the design of the original beam transmitter and receiver.

The beam stations, with the exception of the stations for the Australian circuit, were all designed to utilize two wavelengths, one for daylight working and one for working in the hours of darkness. In the case of the Australian circuit arrangements were made whereby the beam could be directed either way round the world, so that when the communication failed in one direction, the different conditions of light and darkness prevailing the other way round would probably enable working to be resumed.

For the beam stations utilizing two wavelengths a mast system comprising five masts 287 feet high, spaced 650 feet apart was erected. This enabled a beam aerial 1300 feet wide to be used for each wavelength. The concentration of energy from such an aerial was of course in inverse proportion to the length of wave used. These aerials were set at right angles to the actual direction of the great circle, along which the waves travel, between the transmitting station and the receiving station in the distant country. It will be surprising to many people to know in what direction the shortest path lies, for instance, between England and New York and, an even more surprising case, the direction of the shortest route between England and Australia. New York is on about the same latitude as Madrid and one would naturally think therefore that the shortest and most direct route from England to New York would be somewhat south of west : actually the route is very nearly north-west. In the case of Australia the result is even more surprising. As we all know Australia lies in the Southern Pacific Ocean and Melbourne is at the very south of Australia ; who would think that the shortest line from England to Melbourne actually goes nearly 20° north of east, and not in a southerly direction at all ? The Indian station is located near Bombay ; the shortest path, that is to say, the great circle bearing to Bombay in India is almost exactly due east from England. The importance of setting out the line of the aerials where the energy is concentrated in a narrow beam can therefore be appreciated. If the aerials at the transmitting and at the receiving station are set dead true on the great circle bearing the fullest advantage of the strong field radiated at the transmitter and collected at the receiver will be obtained : errors at either end in setting up the aerials are accumulative and the received energy will be proportionally diminished. Very detailed instructions were therefore sent to the engineers in charge at each beam station explaining to them how to fix definitely the position of their stations by means of bearings taken on the sun or certain stars. This was necessary, as, with the degree of accuracy required, compass bearings, with corrections for magnetic variation, would not enable a sufficient degree of accuracy to be attained. The information given to the constructing engineers covered many different methods of making the necessary calculations, and in all cases the aerials were satisfactorily laid out.

The success of a beam station depends to a considerable extent on the care and skill with which the erecting engineer instals the aerials, feeders and transmitting plant ; the results obtained with the beam depend upon the accuracy of the mechanical work put into the construction of the aerial and feeder system, the dimensions of which must adhere strictly to those set out by the designer. Briefly stated, a beam station has three essential wireless links, the multiple aerial system, the feeder system, and the transmitter or receiver, the first two features being the same for either a transmitting or receiving station. The purpose of the feeder is to convey energy without loss from a transmitter to the multiple aerial system, or in the case of the receiving station from the multiple aerial system to the receiver.

The directive properties of the beam aerial, as designed by Franklin in the grid form, are produced by a system of multiple aerials, some of which are fed directly through the feeder from the transmitter and some of which are impulsed indirectly. The wires fed directly are called aerials and those impulsed indirectly are called reflectors. The Marconi beam aerial system consists of a number of active aerials, spaced in a line at right angles to the direction of communication, with a second line of reflector wires a quarter or three-quarters of a wavelength behind the aerial line. When all the aerial wires are fed from a common source of energy, so that the current in every aerial wire has the same phase, fields will be produced which add together in a direction at right angles to the line of the aerial wires. In other directions the fields

from the aerial wires will not add up but produce interference
effects, the result of which forms a beam in both directions
at right angles to the line of aerial wires. A second line of
aerial wires (the reflector) all fed in phase with one another
would produce a similar polar diagram to the first. If both
lines are fed at the same time from a transmitter located at
the aerial line and the second line is fed in antiphase to the
first, since there exists a phase difference between the lines
of 90° because the lines are $\frac{1}{4}$ wavelength apart, the effect
will therefore be for the fields to add in the direction forward
to the active aerial wires, and to cancel behind.

The length of line of aerial wires determines the width of
the beam of radiation, and the greater the number of wires
making up the line the more nearly will the actual shape of
the polar diagram correspond to the theoretical shape, but
the more aerials there are the greater is the difficulty to
provide a feeder system, and in practice it has been
found adequate if the wires be spaced just under half a
wavelength apart. The reflector wires, as they are not fed
directly, can be double or treble the number in the aerial
line.

So far the beam effect " in plan " has been considered, but
it is necessary to consider the radiation from short wave
aerial systems in the zenithal plane also. The purely horizontal wave, called the direct ray, is quickly attenuated, due
to the very high earth losses, to a negligible amount and
cannot be used therefore for long distance communication.
It has been found that the best zenithal angle at which to
propagate short waves for long range communication, *i.e.*
distances over 2000 miles, is between 10° and 15° from the
horizontal, the angle increasing as the distance becomes
shorter.

A single short vertical aerial, with loading to give a node
of potential at the earth, gives maximum radiation at about
50° ; the angle comes down to 45° when the aerial becomes
a half wave aerial. If the length of the aerial is increased
to multiples of half waves without phasing coils, thus forming
what is known as a harmonic aerial, high angle radiation is
still produced, but if phasing coils are inserted between each
half wave then we obtain a series of half wave aerials, all

oscillating in phase, and the zenithal angle is reduced to the angle required.

The Franklin aerial employs this principle, either by using phasing coils, or in later designs, known as the Uniform aerial, by giving the aerial a zig-zag form whereby a non-radiating phase reversing device is obtained. Such an aerial system can be designed to give great concentration of energy, not only in the right direction but also at the correct zenithal angle for best reflection. The design of the feeder system has an important function in the efficient working of a beam station. It must be remembered that the aerial system for each wavelength used on the beam system was supported by three masts each set 650 feet apart ; the face of the aerial was therefore about 1200 feet wide. The aerial wires had each to be energized in phase together, and the problem was to provide a means of conveying the energy from the transmitter to the aerial, so that the length of feeder to each aerial wire should be identical, and to avoid losses in the feeder itself. The feeder as finally designed consisted of concentric copper tubes, air insulated to keep down dielectric losses ; the inner tube, which is the conductor, is kept in position by porcelain spacing insulators, the outer tube is earthed and carried on iron supports about four feet apart, driven into the ground. The feeder from the transmitter is common to every aerial wire for a considerable distance. It is brought to the centre of the aerial system and then branches to two new points ; these two points each branch again, making four new points, each of which can again be teed off, making eight new points. The final number of branches is determined by the total number of wires in the aerial. Each final terminal ends under a pair of aerial wires. If every branch of this tee system is made perfectly symmetrical it is clear that the length of feeder from the common point to each terminal point will be the same, and hence the careful erection of a mechanically accurate feeder system will ensure the desired electrical result; any small inequalities in length, however, particularly in the first two branches, would throw one half of the aerial out of phase. The correct termination of the various branches from the final adjustment to the aerial to the various points from which they bifurcate requires careful adjustment to obtain the correct impedance throughout the feeder system, to avoid reflection in the feeder. At every tee point therefore a transformer is necessary, whereby the correct values of impedance can be obtained.

Among the many stringent conditions laid down in the Imperial Beam Contract was one which required a seven days' test during which each circuit had to function at the high speed of 100 words per minute or over, for the specified number of hours each day.

The actual dates when the Imperial Beam Stations were opened for service after completing their acceptance trials are given in the Appendix together with their call signs and wavelengths used at that time.

Competitors of the Marconi Company abroad had naturally been watching the progress of the short wave development with considerable interest, and in most cases with considerable scepticism. They realized the many unknown factors and difficulties that would have to be overcome, and doubt was expressed as to whether the radiation from a beam aerial would retain directive form when reflected from the Heaviside layer over great distances. The instantaneous success of the beam installations was entirely unexpected by them, and they suddenly realized that not only was there a highly efficient and profitable system of world wide communication in operation, but its efficiency and effectiveness was so far in advance of long wave communication systems that the whole technique of wireless long distance communication must be changed. All foreign organizations had therefore to enter this new field of development, and two of the main competitors of the Marconi Company bought beam transmitters, receivers, and aerials, while their research workers devised modifications of the Franklin aerial system, although based in principle on the Franklin model. During the past five years since the first beam circuit was opened short wave directional work has been rapidly developed in every country, and the very high speed and accuracy of communication effected on the beam circuits has profoundly changed the methods of world communication.

The effect of the inauguration of the Beam services upon the traffic receipts of the Cable Companies was very serious, especially on those routes where previously there had been no wireless competition. Considering the importance of the cable system to the British Empire from the strategic point of view, apart altogether from its great reliability, the Government called together the Cable and Wireless interests, and finally, after long discussions, a merger of interest was brought about, whereby the Imperial Beam services also reverted to private enterprise.

At the present time, with imperial and foreign communications controlled from one centre, effective economies in the handling of traffic have been brought about and new wireless channels brought into service. Since the merging of these interests direct beam communication has been established between Rhodesia and England, between Nairobi in East Africa and England, and wireless telephony has been installed at the South African and Egyptian telegraph stations, and is in progress of construction in India for direct telephonic communication with the Post Office telephone stations at Rugby. Furthermore, a direct telephone service has been established between Bermuda and New York, and plans have been prepared for the extension of the wireless network in many other directions.

On the scientific and technical side much new knowledge and progress has been attained, the careful study of the hours of high speed working on the various wireless routes, the times when fading takes place, the effect of magnetic storms on electro-magnetic radiation, the change in the length of the optimum wavelength during the various seasons of the year, and from year to year, have all been carefully collated, and much valuable information obtained whereby improvements have been made in existing circuits, or in the preparation of plans for future stations.

Other developments made in recent years include the transmission of two or more services on the same aerial with small differences of wavelength, without mutual interference. Actually telephony from one transmitter, and telegraphy from another, have been effected from the same aerial without difficulty. Another development was the provision of multiplex working whereby two separate telegraph channels and one telephone channel were all worked simultaneously from the same transmitter and on the same aerial, and received at the distant station on the same receiving aerial and receiver without mutual interference, but although this method was worked to Canada and to South Africa, the decision of the Government that wireless telephony in England should be operated by the Post Office led to the abandonment of multiplex effected in this manner.

In the later stations erected, economies have been effected by placing the receiving and transmitting aerials on the same site, and housing the receivers and transmitting plant in the same building. No trouble has been experienced thereby.

Many modifications have been made in the details of the transmitting and receiving equipment to the plant as originally installed at the Imperial beam stations ; it would be strange if it were not so after five or six years, but the experience gained of the apparatus then installed has emphasized the good quality of the original work done and the intuition and technical foresight of Marconi and Franklin. The difficulties in communication that have since been encountered, and the future improvements in communication that may be possible, are further discussed in a subsequent chapter on communications.

PLATE X

SHORT-WAVE TRANSMITTERS AT DORCHESTER

[face p. 95

Chapter IX

MODERN COMMERCIAL WIRELESS STATIONS IN ENGLAND

APART from the important field of transatlantic and long range wireless communication, there was a wide scope for the use of wireless to link up various European centres, and supplement the existing network of landline and submarine cable communication. The distances involved did not necessitate the use of large powers, and the knowledge obtained during the years of transatlantic wireless experiments was available.

Wireless traffic operating companies had been formed in a number of European countries, some controlled by the Marconi Company, others closely associated with that Company by agreements and mutual interests. The British Post Office granted licences under certain restrictions to the Marconi Company to establish wireless services with France, Spain, Switzerland, Austria, and elsewhere. It was therefore decided to build a number of transmitting and receiving stations as near as possible to London, and to establish a Central Telegraph Control Office in London, from where all the various transmitters, including those at Carnarvon, and the receivers working on the different circuits could be controlled and operated. A site, capable of accommodating all the contemplated transmitters and transmitting aerials for the European services, with room for further extensions in the future, was selected at North Weald, Ongar, and a receiving site was chosen at Brentwood.

For the Central Wireless Telegraph Office a suitable building was acquired in Water Street, off Moorgate Street, in the City, which became the public and distribution centre for all wireless traffic.

At Ongar, the new transmitting centre, three widely separated aerial systems were erected supported by masts 300 feet high, and at the foot of each mast system a building was erected to accommodate one or more transmitters. Four long wave transmitters were installed for European communications. In one building two transmitters of 10 kw. and 5 kw. input respectively were erected, and arranged to work simultaneously on a common aerial, anti-coupling coils being provided to avoid reaction from one transmitter to the other. The other two transmitters in separate buildings were of 25 and 15 kw. capacity. In 1931 another larger long wave transmitter of 110 kw. capacity and 9630 metres wavelength, was erected by the Marconi Company for the Communication Company. All these five transmitters are of the valve type, and are now provided with valve drives to ensure constancy of wavelength. Recently further extensions have been carried out at Ongar, and the original long wave transmitters have been replaced by transmitters of more modern types, and all the transmitters have been housed in one central building on the site, the high frequency energy from each transmitter being carried by long feeders to the respective aerials. In addition to the long wave transmitters a number of short wave transmitters have been erected at Ongar   Shortly after the successful demonstration of the great value of short wave communication by the performances of the beam stations it was decided to erect two short wave transmitters for supplementary services at Ongar ; one of these worked on a wavelength of 27·45 metres, and consisted of a simple self oscillator, using about 6 kw. ; the other using a wavelength of 15 metres was provided with a drive, and employed about 8 kws. to the anode of the valves. They both worked on simple omnidirectional aerials.

In the reorganization and extension of the Ongar transmitters which has recently been effected these transmitters have been replaced or remodelled in accordance with the latest technical developments.

The convenient position of Ongar, near London, served by short land lines and within easy access, made it the obvious transmitting centre for all future extensions, up to the limit of the capacity of the site. When it was decided to establish wireless direct services with Nairobi in East Africa, and with Southern Rhodesia, the beam transmitting stations were erected at Ongar. At the same time it was decided to extend the transmitting facilities to New York, and two more beam transmitters for New York services were erected at Ongar. All these short wave transmitters were designed for a capacity of 25 kw. to the anodes of the transmitting valves. In addition to these transmitters yet another larger transmitter was constructed to employ 40 kws. to the anodes and designed to work on any of four different wavelengths, with means for changing the wavelength in a few seconds to any of the four selected waves. This transmitter is used on facsimile transmission, and also to assist on any circuit where difficulties in clearing traffic may be experienced.

A table giving the list of the Ongar transmitters with their call letters and wavelengths, and the services which they normally carry out, will be found in the Appendix. Frequently, however, a transmitter is switched off its normal service for communication with some other station, and all the transmitters which normally work on beam aerials can be switched on to omnidirectional aerials if required.

The Receiving centre, corresponding to the Transmitting centre at Ongar, is situated at Brentwood, about six miles distant from the Ongar transmitting station. This receiving station was originally built for the reception of the European services on the long wavelengths. In 1923 the long wave reception from America, which up to that date had been carried out at Towyn, was transferred to Brentwood and the operators all accommodated at the London Central Control Office ~. Radio House. The incoming traffic at Brentwood was all relayed to Radio House, which became the controlling centre for all wireless outgoing and incoming traffic. Since the merging of the cable and wireless interests, the central wireless telegraph office has been transferred from Radio House to Electra House, so that all cable and wireless services can be centrally controlled.

As the number of short wave services has grown, the Brentwood receiving station has been gradually equipped with short wave receivers and aerials to cope with this short wave traffic ; the Australian and Indian reception is still carried out at the Beam Receiving Station at Skegness, the

G

Canadian and South African reception at Bridgwater, and the Somerton Station is used for beam reception from New York, Buenos Aires, Rio, Japan and Egypt, but the Brentwood station frequently helps in the reception on some of these circuits, and its use is being gradually extended for reception on new circuits as they are developed. There are eight long wave, eight medium, and thirteen short wave receivers installed at Brentwood, while seven more short wave receivers are about to be installed to cope with the ever-growing number of communications. The Brentwood aerial equipment is necessarily of a very diverse character, and illustrates the progressive change in design which the development of wireless technique is constantly bringing about. The aerials for the long wave reception are supported by four masts 200 feet high erected in the form of a 450-feet square. These masts support two frame aerials. There are also four other 90-feet towers, symmetrically placed, which support the aerials for the continental services. Each aerial is given a heart-shaped diagram of reception, in which the direction of the strongest reception corresponds to the direction of the station from which communication is desired, radiogoniometers being provided with each receiver. The signals from all the transatlantic stations are received on one aerial, and all the continental services are received on the other common aerial.

For short wave reception there are provided two wide angle Franklin Uniform aerials without reflectors for use on the short wave Berne and Madrid services, and three directional aerials of the type evolved by the Radio Corporation of America ; one of these is used for reception from New York, Vienna, and Beyreuth, another for reception from Siam, and the third for reception from Lisbon, Rio de Janeiro, and Japan. There are also available four omnidirectional short wave aerials for general purposes. For the services with Nairobi and South Rhodesia, beam receiving aerials have been erected, while further directive aerials are about to be erected for reception from the United States, and from seven different countries. When all these aerials are completed and the new receivers installed, bringing up the total receiver equipment to 36, the Brentwood receiving centre will be one of the most important and interesting equipments in wireless communication services.

Whereas the signals received at Brentwood are sent direct to the central control office at Electra House, where the operators are located, it is necessary that Brentwood should be able to check the quality of any incoming signal ; monitoring arrangements are provided, therefore, so that the signals from any receiver can be checked, either by telephone or by any of the three undulators provided. Furthermore, all signals sent out from Electra House to operate the Ongar transmitters over the landlines, which pass in and out of the Brentwood station, can be checked there, as can also the signals radiated from any of the transmitters at Ongar.

Although Ongar is gradually becoming an important short wave as well as a long wave transmitting centre, the main beam transmitting centre is at Dorchester. This station is provided with eight short wave transmitters and is the transmitting centre for a number of important services. The aerials are on the Beam system. A row of five masts is erected on the line at right angles to the great circle bearing on New York, supporting four bays of beam aerials in the direction of New York, and in the opposite direction two bays of beam aerials for communication to Egypt. Where aerials have been erected, as in this case for transmission in two opposite directions, a common central reflector is used, and if the direction, as in the case of Egypt, is not exactly on the continuation of the great circle from New York through the station, then the aerial can be and is electrically swung by adjustments of the feeder system, so that, by slightly altering the phasing between the wires composing the beam aerial, the angle of the beam can be shifted a few degrees off the right angle to the face of the beam aerial. Another pair of masts supports a beam aerial for working to Rio and Buenos Aires, while a further three masts provide two bays, one for working with South America on a second wavelength, and one for communication with Japan. The power to the transmitters is obtained from a common high tension direct current supply, furnished by high tension direct current generators at about 7500 volts ; each machine is capable of providing 10,000 volts if required.

The transmitters are all provided with the latest Franklin constant frequency drive, and every modern improvement has been embodied in the equipment of these transmitters. The transmitters are controlled from tables placed along the centre line of the hall, and all these transmitters can be efficiently looked after by two men. The control of the operation of the transmitters is carried out from the Central Telegraph Office in London, which is directly connected to the Dorchester station by a number of land lines. The chief services carried out by the Dorchester station are with New York, Rio de Janeiro, Buenos Aires, Japan, and Egypt. Means are provided for checking both the incoming signals over the land line and the signals radiated from the aerials. For this purpose two monitoring recorders are provided, and these can be plugged into any of the incoming lines, or outgoing transmitter signals. Precision wavemeters are also provided and a frequent check is taken on each circuit, to ensure that no misadjustment of frequency has taken place.

The complementary receiving station to the transmitting centre at Dorchester is the station at Somerton. Originally this station was equipped with two rows of masts supporting beam aerials for communication with New York and South America. The aerial system has subsequently been considerably altered and extended, and the mast system now supports sixteen different aerials. These include four beam aerials for reception from New York, two beam aerials for reception of the day and night waves from Egypt, two similar aerials for reception from Buenos Aires, and two for Rio de Janeiro reception. There are three beam aerials for reception from Japan, one for auxiliary reception from Australia, and two aerials for general purposes. The aerials are so arranged that on some of the wavelengths on certain circuits diversity reception can be effected, so that the advantage of beam reception is further augmented and quick fading reduced. The feeders from all these aerials are led to a common feeder box, built on the Swiss commutator principle, whereby any aerial can be connected to any receiver. Fourteen high speed commercial receivers are installed.

Mention has been made in previous paragraphs of the Central Telegraph Office, now situated at Electra House, in

Moorgate, from which land lines radiate to all the wireless telegraph transmitting and receiving stations, and which also forms the terminus of all the cables operated by Imperial and International Communications Limited.

The Central Telegraph Office is the " nerve centre " of the world system of Cables and Wireless, controlled by the Communication Company, and on its efficient equipment and organization largely depend the financial result from the traffic passing over the system, and the speed with which such traffic can be handled.

In the early days of wireless communication the stations were built on the coasts, on sites selected so that the signals traversed the shortest possible distance, and with as little land as possible intervening, consequently the stations had to be erected at considerable distances from the cities where the traffic originated. Telegraph landlines were therefore required between the cities and the stations, and their length, and sometimes quality, combined with the type of wireless signal then received, prevented direct relaying of these signals on to the land lines.

It may be remarked that in the first transatlantic wireless service between Clifden and Glace Bay the wireless stations were often out of touch with each other, but it is doubtful whether these wireless interruptions were any more frequent than those which occurred on the land line between Clifden, in Ireland, and London and between Glace Bay and Montreal. The stoppages not being necessarily coincident, the need for some sort of traffic storage at the wireless stations was obvious. It was for such reasons that an operating staff, capable of handling the whole of the traffic, was required at the wireless station as well as at the City Office.

Actually technical reasons barred the way to direct retransmission. Received signals were of such a quality that they could be relayed over telephone lines but not over telegraph lines. Long distance telephone lines had not been developed to the places where the wireless stations were built, and so the links to these stations had to be made by telegraph lines.

Methods of operating a telegraph relay by a wireless signal waited on the production of suitable valves. The high speed wireless signals were dealt with by recording on " Dictaphone" records, which were then run at slow speeds for transcription by the wireless operator. On the first wireless continental circuit from London to Paris high speeds were anticipated as the normal method of working over so short a wireless link, and a first attempt was made at direct operation between the two cities. The receiving telegraph relay required a bank of ten small receiving valves for its operation from the wireless signal, but as far as London was concerned the foundation of a Central Wireless Control Office was laid.

More suitable valves and improved receivers, coupled with short landlines to stations near London, very soon consolidated the direct central control of services to European points, on which good signals were almost invariably obtained. With the transatlantic wireless services progress was not so rapid. Signals could be relayed on to telegraph lines, but in so doing the characteristic difference between signals and atmospherics was lost, and aural discrimination, which had been performed by the wireless operator, could no longer be relied upon. The solution was either to provide good telephone lines to the distant wireless stations or to move the receiving stations near to the city. The latter course was adopted, and the receiving centre at Brentwood extended for transatlantic reception. As a result of this the operators in the Central Office were able to listen to the actual wireless signal, and to carry on their laborious task of differentiating between signals coming from America or Canada and atmospherics originating probably over the Sahara, while at adjacent tables Creed automatic printers thumped out perfect signals at 100 words per minute from Paris and other European centres.

The centralizing of reception at one Receiving Centre, and the relaying of the receiving signal into the Central Office, brought about a great reduction in the number of operators required on a wireless circuit and reduced the delays imposed by the wireless link to a negligible amount compared with the delays in handling the traffic in the Central Office. The Central Telegraph Office was obliged to cater for varying classes of circuits from high speed printer and transcription from recorder tape, to slow speed aural working on the transoceanic circuits. Long distance wireless communication had yet to come into its own.

Much of the usual complement of a Telegraph Office was used to speed up the handling of wireless messages ; pneumatic tubes and various types of mechanical message carriers, and automatic means for the timing of messages at various points, were installed so that abnormal delay could be traced and rectified. But behind all this was the uncertainty of wireless conditions. Seconds of delay, saved by keen organization, were swept away and swamped by the vagaries of atmospheric storms, with no alternative route available, and only limited capacity on the long distance circuits when normal conditions were restored. All this allowed no margin for poor control lines, faulty transmitters, or inferior receivers, and the elimination of all these difficulties was the subject of constant research.

Greater flexibility and economy of landlines showed the need for relaying all signals to the Central Office at audio frequencies over telephone lines, and equipment was soon developed for doing this. The valve operated converters, for working the telegraph relays and recorders, were installed at the Central Office instead of at the Receiving stations, and at all times the actual wireless signal, whether or not suitable for recording, was available in the operating department at the Central Office.

This was an important step, since dual reception, recorder and aural, was now economically possible, and even on the long distance circuits advantage could be taken of all periods of improved conditions to increase the working speeds beyond that of the individual operator, or to augment the operator's speed and accuracy by making simultaneously available to him both aural and recorder signals.

A very specialized form of operating thus grew up and staff were trained to apply this system to all circuits ; so successfully indeed that it soon became obvious that, in the interests of standardization and accuracy, the printer system could be superseded by the newer system of direct typewriting on to the delivery forms of the telegram received by aural and recorder slip signals. This was a setback to machine telegraphy applied to wireless, but it was in the immediate interests of commercial wireless telegraphy.

The advent of the Beam Short Wave system was very far reaching in its effects on Central Office organization. To those operating concerns who already worked high speed short distance circuits the new high speed beam circuits involved no great change of practice, but their internal organizations had to be extended to those services previously operated on slow speed long waves. Other Corporations however who had conducted only slow speed services were faced with a complete reorganization of the Control Traffic Centres, and therefore shared in the revolution of wireless telegraph ideas, for which in fact the Beam system was responsible.

Whereas much higher speeds over long periods were now made possible it could not be said that the stability of circuits was yet ensured. Rather did the new system enable new circuits hitherto impracticable to be opened. As a result the attempts to revert to machine telegraphy failed, and the well-established method of typing from recorder slip held firmly its superiority in the new field. Certain beam circuits however displayed a high degree of stability and freedom from interference, to an extent that might justify machine telegraphy, when a suitable system for wireless signals could be developed. This came later. One of the chief effects of the successful application of short wave wireless telegraphy was the fact that long distance services could be operated comparatively cheaply even if the traffic loads were light, and this meant that every Administration could conduct direct services to every other Administration, and do so economically. The effect on the old main traffic carrying arteries is obvious. Central Office practice had to adapt itself to a mushroom growth of small circuits, and the problem of organization to limit the tendency of increased internal delays became one of necessary and immediate solution.

As the capabilities and limitations of short wave working became better known and the performance on any particular circuit could be calculated with reliability, wireless began to cater for certain classes of preferred traffic to which adequate service had, in the past, been given only by cables. This class of traffic requires handling at the terminal stations by special private lines, telegraph, telephone and teleprinter, and these special forms of delivery and collection had to be brought into the closest possible harmony with the wireless circuits in the Central Control Office. In these rapid services seconds are of importance, and the central control of the wireless links concerned had to be developed and maintained by specially trained staff with a knowledge of daily and seasonal changes in wireless conditions.

The merging of the Cable and Wireless interests had a profound effect on Central Office Control and organization. The well-established cables were already operating almost completely on machine telegraphy ; both systems could contribute something in efficient handling of traffic which was new to the other. More than ever was internal delay the chief problem to be solved. With larger offices, and more intricate transit routes between all the services, the delay at the terminals bid fair to swamp that on the circuit itself, however good or bad the characteristics of the latter might be. The first big change in organization was to move the wireless circuits from Radio House to Electra House, so that all the cable and wireless circuits could be located together. As a result of the amalgamation of the services and a careful study of the problem of avoiding all possible delays, the Central Control Office at Electra House has been equipped with all the modern methods of checking, distributing, timing, and transporting of telegrams.

To simplify these operations much of the equipment associated with the transmission and reception of signals has been removed from the operating tables, and has been centralized in a special section under the maintenance and control of a special staff of technicians who are in direct and constant touch with the actual wireless station. This section contains in particular all the valve amplifiers and relay convertors, all control lines with testing and distributing apparatus, and the whole of this equipment has been erected to allow of easy access and maintenance.

Mention has been made of the early failure of machine telegraphy on wireless circuits, but the well-tried system in use on the cables shows definite promise of success on certain of the Beam circuits. The actual elimination of false signals cannot yet be contemplated; a system, however, is already in use which enables the checking operator to appreciate false signals before the telegram is delivered to the addressee. The older printing methods failed to do this. Provided therefore that the wireless circuit is sufficiently stable to reduce the actual number of false signals to a level which can be dealt with economically by corrections, machine telegraphy can now be applied with those definite economies in staff of which the cables have already taken advantage. Quite recently the typewriting telegraph has been developed for land wire working in such a way that the customer can become his own operator, and by dialling the number of his correspondent on his ordinary telephone, is almost immediately in communication with him. So far this is confined to inland telegraph connections, but with the perfection of machine telegraphy on wireless the extension of such a service to all parts of the world is perhaps only a question of time.

A description of modern commercial wireless stations in England would not be complete without reference to the big wireless transmitting centre constructed by the British Post Office at Rugby. Although the Rugby station does not fulfil its original intention of providing radio telegraphic commercial services to all parts of the Empire, it yet fulfils a very important function in broadcasting news, in providing ships with Time Signals, and Meteorological reports, and long distance messages to ships at sea. The Rugby long wave telegraph transmitter is the most powerful valve transmitter in the world, but the chief importance of the Rugby station is that it is the centre of all radio telephone communication from England. It is equipped with the most modern long and short wave telephone transmitters.

The site of the Rugby station consists of 900 acres, situated about 4 miles south-east of Rugby. The station buildings consist of two groups, the Main Station and the New Station. The power is provided from the public supply at 12,000 volts 50 cycles three phase. The main aerial is supported by twelve masts 820 feet high ; eight of these are arranged in an irregular octagon, while the four others provide two extensions to the north. These masts support the three aerials for the three long wave services in use. The masts are triangular in shape, each side of the triangle being 10 feet wide. The base of each mast terminates in a tripod, the mast therefore being capable of free movement about the lower extremity. The masts are insulated from the ground by means of porcelain and granite insulators. Each mast is supported by fifteen wire rope stays, and the mast is designed to withstand a wind pressure of 140 miles per hour and for a horizontal pull of 10 tons at the top. The masts are placed 440 yards apart.

Each of the long wave transmitters are of the valve type. The main transmitter and the medium power transmitter are controlled in frequency by means of valve-maintained tuning forks. These forks vibrate at audio frequencies, and harmonics of the fork frequencies are selected, and amplified in successive stages, so that the frequency corresponds with that of the wave required to be transmitted. From this stage the power is amplified in power amplifier units to the final output of the transmitter. The power from the tuning fork drive is taken to the first power amplifier, which amplifies to 2 kilowatts, effected by means of glass valves, then to the second stage with an output of 30 kilowatts, the valves used consisting of three 10-kilowatt water-cooled valves, and thence to the final power amplifier, which consists of five panels, each carrying eighteen water-cooled valves, three panels being used to give the maximum output of 540 kilowatts to the aerial. Mention must here be made that the Post Office engineers have recently installed a single large valve, designed by the Metropolitan Vickers Company, which is demountable, that is to say, its electrodes can be replaced when required and the vacuum be renewed. This valve has operated in circuit quite satisfactorily in place of the fifty-four water-cooled valves in the last amplifier, and has delivered over 700 amperes to the aerial with an input of 525 kilowatts.

As regards the long wave telephone transmitter, this utilizes the single side band system of transmission ; by this means the power used is made six times more effective than the same power would be if radiated from an ordinary station such as used for broadcasting : in addition the band of wavelengths used in the ether is halved, so that interference with other stations is reduced to a minimum.

The Rugby transmitting centre is also equipped with a number of short wave telephone transmitters, and a large number of directive aerials have been erected for carrying out the short wave telephone services to distant parts of the world. These are more particularly referred to in the chapter devoted to Post Office Development in Wireless.

CHAPTER X

WIRELESS IN WAR ON LAND

WIRELESS has been employed to an increasing extent in every war since the beginning of the century. The first use made of wireless in military operations was during the South African War, when the British War Office purchased six Marconi sets. These were used to a certain extent in the field, but they were not easily portable, and they were shortly taken over by the Naval Squadron operating in South African waters, where they rendered useful service. Had these sets been available at Ladysmith, Kimberley and Mafeking they would have been of the utmost value to the besieged garrisons. Much controversy has attended the use of wireless for army purposes : arguments arose from the fact that, notwithstanding the obvious services it can render, several serious disadvantages attend the use of wireless with particular force in war. During the Great War, 1914 to 1918, all the advantages and disadvantages were weighed up, and the balance was struck in favour of its usefulness. It may be of interest to state briefly what the arguments are : those in favour of it point out that wireless is peculiarly mobile, and by its use one headquarters can communicate with another without knowing the latter's location. It can accompany a headquarters anywhere, it takes no notice of roads or obstacles, its waves are not interrupted by bullets, shells or transport, nor obstructed by smoke, dust or fog. These factors greatly assist mobility and, since mobility is one of the essential factors of victory, these arguments are very powerful ones. Those against the use of wireless argued that wireless messages can be heard by the enemy, that the direction of a transmitting station can be ascertained by the enemy, and thus the headquarters operating the station located, that a wireless operator requires much training and the apparatus considerable technical supervision before a good organization can be assured, that an enemy can interfere deliberately with the reception of a message by transmitting on the same wavelength, and failures can be expected from the effects on reception of atmospheric disturbances, as well as by human errors. These disadvantages were seriously considered but they are conditional and not fundamental. Experience in war is that what is a disadvantage to one side may be turned to the advantage of the other, and in consequence wireless military services have developed in two different directions, one " communication," concerned with the sending and receiving of messages within the army, the other " observation," consisting in listening to an enemy's communications and locating the position of his transmitting stations. Both of these branches of military wireless are full of interest but, as they differ widely in their functions, it is proposed to treat them separately.

Communications.—The essential requirements from a system of army communications are :—

1. It must be able to be established quickly anywhere, because the user must be free to move anywhere at short notice, and always requires communication at the moment he arrives at a new position.
2. It must be rapid, because delay between the writing and delivery of a message is a grave objection.
3. It must be secret, so as not to disclose to an enemy information which may be of value, immediately or even at a subsequent period.
4. It must be reliable, and not fail when needed.
5. In many cases it must be capable of dealing with a large volume of traffic.

None of the various methods available possess all these features, and in consequence no army can rely on one method only but must use a judicious combination of various methods. The main methods available for modern warfare are—wire and wireless telegraphy and telephony, visual or optical telegraphy (flags, lamps, etc.) and human messengers. Other minor methods used include dogs, pigeons, message rockets, etc. We are not concerned with other methods than wireless, except to emphasize that wireless cannot be expected to supersede them, but will hold its place as one of several methods to be used as circumstances dictate. Generally speaking, the larger an army, the more complex is the system of communication needed. Both causes tend to reduce its mobility, and this in turn renders it possible to construct a network of wires.

Communication by wires (telegraph and telephone) is naturally superior to that by wireless, because a far greater volume of traffic can be dealt with without risk of interference or overhearing, and with much simpler apparatus. Wires, however, are constantly broken by shells, and vehicles, and their repair is costly in human life ; they require much transport to lay and maintain, and they are slow to establish. In consequence, even in conditions where wires can be employed, they cannot be relied upon and must be duplicated by other means.

The use of wireless for army communication developed to its present position almost entirely during the great war, and the subject cannot well be discussed without reference to its war history.

Although trench warfare caused large movements to cease and communication by wire became the normal method, yet the very fact that so much reliance was placed upon wires gave great opportunities to alternative methods when the wires failed. Wireless proved its value as an alternative on many occasions during trench warfare, but it was during the main attacks in the great battles that the most interesting incidents occurred, when wires either could not possibly be laid or were broken up by shell fire as soon as put down and could not be maintained. One of the first instances of this occurred in September 1915 when, during the battle of Loos, a small wireless set was erected in the ruins of the village of Loos, soon after its capture by the British troops. This set was the only means of communication at a critical moment, and was the method by which information was passed vitally affecting the action of the allied cavalry. The battle of Loos was the result of an attack by the British Army simultaneously with a great French attack about twenty miles further south. The object of these attacks was to pierce the German lines ; if a gap was made by the British attack, the

British Cavalry Corps was to be launched through the gap, followed by the French Cavalry, whereas if the French broke through in their attack the British Cavalry were to follow the French in exploiting their success. The early attacks of the British were so successful as to create the impression that the British Cavalry could be brought into action, but in actual fact the German line had not been permanently pierced, and a wireless report to this effect prevented the cavalry from starting on an adventure which would without doubt have been disastrous. There was no means apart from this wireless set of passing on this vital information, and it can be claimed therefore that wireless prevented severe casualties in the British Cavalry, and possibly a disaster which may well have had far-reaching results. This little wireless set rendered further valuable service during the battle. The garrison of Loos, when very hard pressed and contemplating a withdrawal, received information that support was being organized, and the loss of the Loos position by the British was thus avoided. The above incident has been described at some length because it gave an impetus to the employment of wireless by the British Army in the forward areas of battle. Here, owing to the intensity of artillery fire, no means of communication except deeply buried cables can be relied upon and, of course, even in trench warfare it is not possible to construct deeply buried cable routes to keep pace with the early phases of an attack.

Partly as a result of the lesson given by the above incident as to the value of wireless, and no doubt as a result of similar experiences, the use of wireless grew rapidly in all armies, and a number of small wireless sets were issued to the British Army. At that period, however, wireless valves were practically unknown, no set sufficiently robust and portable, utilizing valves as transmitters had been devised, and telegraphy for the army in the field by the spark method was the only means practicable. With spark transmitters only a few sets could be employed on a corps frontage without mutual interference, and the use of wireless was limited and confined to telegraphy. Later, in 1918, small wireless transmitters using thermionic valves were designed and supplied, thus introducing the use of continuous waves and making possible the employment of a larger number of stations on the front.

Subsequent to the war there has been a great development in the reliability of valve transmitters and in the selectivity of wireless receivers, with the result that at the present day (1933) wireless transmitters and receivers are manufactured for army purposes using both telegraphy and telephony, and it is possible to employ them without causing mutual interference, far more closely together than could be effected during the war; thus a new technique has grown up which renders the practice of the great war obsolete. Nevertheless, the lessons learned in war, if considered in relation to the principles involved, are fundamental, and in spite of the fact that present-day wireless technique differs radically from that in use in war days, it is thought that a few more incidents and details regarding war communications may be of interest.

It has already been stated that there are two great disadvantages in the use of wireless in war, namely enemy interception and direction finding, and these tend to create a feeling of insecurity and distrust in the minds of Commanding Officers. The risk of being overheard is a particularly dangerous feature in military communication : in trench warfare especially, when time allows for the perfection of an intercepting organization, there is a grave danger that wireless messages will be received by the enemy, and that their contents may be communicated rapidly to his troops, but in periods of mobility it is much less likely that a message is overheard, and the risk much smaller that the information can be communicated in time for effective counteraction to be taken. This is due to several causes. Firstly, delay will occur in transmitting the contents of an intercepted message from a wireless observation station through the staff channels to the Commander who can act on the information, and such delays are bound to be longer during periods of mobility than in periods of trench warfare. Secondly, during mobile operations the enemy wireless communication service which is in close touch with the troops will itself be occupied and unable to intercept. Thirdly, it usually takes longer to arrange counteraction when troops are mobile than when they are entrenched and in the meantime the situation may be changing so rapidly as to render counteraction abortive. Nevertheless, the danger of overhearing is ever present and cannot be neglected with impunity. The methods employed to mitigate this disadvantage comprise cypher, code and secret technical devices, but the most important is a firm control of the employment of wireless by the staff. Cypher is a slow process, requiring extra personnel, and seriously handicaps the efficiency of communication : for example, a message of 200 letters in plain language can generally be received correctly without repetition in two or three minutes, whereas to encipher such a message by hand will take about ten minutes, to send the message in cypher will take about five minutes, and about ten minutes would be occupied in deciphering it, a total of twenty-five minutes. Code is of two kinds, the use of code books by which sentences and words are substituted by short groups of letters or figures, and the use of code words or letter groups to represent foreseen circumstances, map positions, times, units, names, etc. The former kind of code is slow to use and unsafe owing to the risk of capture of a code book ; the second kind of code is very limited in its application, because all circumstances that might arise cannot be foreseen, moreover to be safe it must frequently be changed.

Secret technical devices are generally complex and bulky and are not suitable for use by portable stations, but they do not delay messages and are reasonably safe. Control by the staff cannot ensure secrecy, but by sending out false messages from time to time it may be possible to cause an enemy to distrust the information he overhears and therefore not take action on information which may be genuine. The risk of direction finding is also an ever present one, but the danger is often exaggerated. In the case of small mobile wireless stations with a range of only a few kilometres the danger is not great. A direction finding equipment in the field is of limited use unless it forms part of a system requiring an elaborate organization. It is therefore difficult to establish this in the field during period of mobility, but during periods of trench warfare it was found quite possible to create an efficient organization. A direction finding instrument is not instantaneous in action, even when taking one bearing only.

Owing to technical reasons errors sometimes occur and one bearing is not sufficient, several must be averaged. Under the best conditions, when given sufficient opportunity, good equipment, well-trained operators, and an efficient organization, the average bearing on a transmitting station can be expected to have an accuracy within about one or two degrees, or say 300 metres in a range of 10 kilometres. This is not of sufficient accuracy to direct artillery fire on the target, but it is enough to assist an aeroplane to locate the station exactly if it is not concealed. This possible danger is rather a contingent than an absolute one and does not outweigh the advantages of wireless for communication.

To return to the subject of wireless communication, it will be appreciated that the message traffic in an army at war varies very greatly in type between long messages over long distances, which characterizes the traffic between headquarters of the larger formations, and short messages over short distances, of which the traffic is generally comprised between headquarters of small formations and within units. Moreover, the permissible delay varies between an hour or more in the case of the former class to a minute or so for the latter. The consequences resulting from the overhearing or direction finding of the larger wireless stations are greater than for the smaller stations, and the difficulties of maintaining communications by means other than wireless are greater with small units and formations than with the larger ones, on account of their increased mobility and proximity to the enemy. In consequence there is a tendency to the employment of wireless more and more in the forward battle areas by the fighting troops for tactical purposes.

In the Great War the British Army was equipped in 1916 with so-called trench sets, but as these used aerials 10 feet or more in height to obtain a useful range, they could only be erected in selected situations and also, owing to the need of avoiding mutual interference, their numbers had to be limited to about one set per Divisional front. These stations were genarally placed at important tactical points where other communication was difficult, and whence each could serve the headquarters of two or three infantry battalions. Three or four of these worked back to one central station, which was in telephonic communication with all Divisional headquarters. When an attack took place the forward wireless sets would be moved forward into the captured position. During the fighting on the Somme in the autumn of 1916 these wireless sets (and pigeons) were sometimes the only way of bridging the enemy artillery barrage, in which neither human messengers nor wires could exist. Thus attacking troops were able to report their positions in cypher and call for artillery support when counter-attacked. An interesting and important point arising from the use of wireless sets with attacking troops was the timing of the advance. Each set required a party of three pairs of men for their transport over the broken muddy crater fields. One casualty delayed the whole station and the party was necessarily conspicuous because pairs of men, carrying loads, differed in appearance from the individual infantry. Consequently if the wireless set went with one of the attacking waves it was not likely to reach its destination, as it was at once singled out for machine gun fire ; on the other hand, if the wireless set followed behind the attack it was liable to get involved in the enemy's artillery barrage. The wretched operators were therefore in an unhappy position. This was remedied in 1917 and 1918, when new types of equipment became available, smaller and more compact, and arranged for transport as knapsacks, thus rendering the operators less conspicuous on the battlefield, as they now looked the same as the other men. These newer sets had less power than the earlier types, they employed shorter waves and had valve receivers ; it was therefore possible to use them more closely on the front without causing mutual interference. They were actually employed, two to each infantry brigade, a much better organization than the 1916 Corps control.

In the successful large scale attacks of Cambrai November 1917, St. Quentin March 1918, the Aisne May and June 1918, and the final defeat of the German Army between August and November 1918, the rapid advances and retreats involved brought the use of wireless very much to the fore. Not only did the movements of headquarters sometimes outpace the rate at which wires could be laid, but no wires could be provided for lateral communication.

Some wireless stations dealt with over 100 messages a day, in addition to moving and re-erecting the station more than once, and this in spite of a great deal of interference by other stations, both friendly and hostile. In circumstances such as these the rapidity with which the situation changed rendered overhearing less dangerous and the use of cypher or code was often discarded.   Wireless in clear language was used to report enemy action and to direct artillery fire.   Short codes were used to notify positions of the front and the movements of headquarters by time and place.   Situation reports and even operation orders were dealt with.   At some times the wireless traffic became so intensive that enemy overhearing organizations were only able to cope with a small fraction of the messages passed, the bulk therefore being rendered safe by its own profusion.

Thus the lesson was learned that, in spite of its disadvantages, wireless as a means of communication cannot be neglected, and is essential when much mobility is taking place.

Military Wireless Telephony.

The advent of the thermionic valve as a practical wireless transmitter has made it possible to construct small sets for telephony as well as telegraphy.   This has created an interesting situation from a military point of view but one that has as yet not been subjected to war experience.   The use of telephony simplifies the training of operating personnel, since it obviates the necessity of a knowledge of Morse code, but on the other hand it raises other difficulties in regard to overhearing, and must impose even more care than before in the operation of wireless under war conditions.   Where the language of two belligerents is different telephony may be safer than telegraphy, because, unlike the Morse code, it cannot be recorded without shorthand or elaborate apparatus; the risk involved will no doubt be carefully analysed and faced in any future war.

For short range sets with forward troops, where action follows swiftly on messages, the risk of being overheard and understood will often be small, but with long range wireless telephony the danger will be great.   Secret telephony confers a certain degree of immunity from being overheard and understood, but it is only possible with well-found, expensive and permanent installations. It does not seem probable that telephony will be much used in future wars except by forward troops, unless some simple device for ensuring real secrecy is invented.

Observation.

This branch of military wireless consists almost entirely in receiving from the enemy, although it has other important uses in aircraft and naval service. It had immense importance in the Great War and it appears probable that it will always be an important part of any military wireless organization. It includes two spheres of utility which overlap, namely, interception and direction finding.

Interception consists not only in eavesdropping and receiving the enemy's messages but also in recording any noticeable characteristics of his equipment, operating personnel, and methods from which subsequent information can be gleaned. Direction finding consists in recording call signs and azimuth bearings of enemy wireless stations. The co-ordination of such information obtained by two or more bearings, taken by two or more direction finding sets in different locations, enables a plan to be made showing the approximate positions and the actual grouping of the radio stations, and consequently of the formations in the enemy army.

The employment of a wireless observational group in an army thus provides a source of valuable information to the staff and imposes restrictions and handicaps upon the enemy's communications. Furthermore, as it exists to take advantage of the indiscreet use of wireless by the enemy, it also serves as a check to prevent indiscretions in the use of wireless in its own army.

A most interesting example of the value of interception and the danger of the indiscreet use of wireless communication occurred in 1914 on the Russo-German front, and led to the battle of Tannenberg. It will be recalled that the Russian armies were invading East Prussia in two groups, one under Rennenkampf from the east, and one under Samsonoff from the south. The Germans with inferior numbers were in danger of being defeated. After slightly checking Rennenkampf at the indecisive but severe action of Gumbinnen, the Germans retired but were uncertain as to what course to adopt. Suddenly a Russian wireless message disclosed the intention of Rennenkampf to continue his advance rather slowly towards the fortress of Koenigsberg, *i.e.* in a westerly direction ; instead of cooperating closely with Samsonoff by a movement south-westward. A second wireless message gave away Samsonoff's plans. On this intercepted information of the Russian plans the Germans decided that they had time to utilize their superior mobility in order to attack Samsonoff before Rennenkampf could come to his assistance. They did so and gained the overwhelming victory of Tannenberg, in which Samsonoff's army was completely destroyed. It is interesting to speculate as to how history might have been different if the Germans had not intercepted these fateful Russian messages, for the victory of Tannenberg and its consequence, the defeat of Rennenkampf, relieved the German armies of the Russian menace and as a result of these victories, large German forces were released for use on other fronts.

The above incident is probably the supreme example of the misuse of wireless, and shows the great importance of an efficient intercepting organization being ready to seize a fleeting opportunity. Many other dramatic incidents can be quoted from the Great War. For instance, in October 1914, when the Franco-British armies were engaged in the attempt to outflank the German army between Laon and the Belgian coast, a German wireless message was received by a fixed station in England, the Leafield station near Oxford, disclosing plans for an attack by a comparatively small German force. This information was immediately telephoned to France and the French high command were able to take counter measures to enable the threatened attack to be broken up before it was fully launched. To quote another incident. The British army form in the early months of the war had included on it spaces for Message from................ Place................ Time..........and the training instructions stressed the importance of the originator completing this information, which is obviously essential in mobile conditions : on the other hand, the regulations insisted that such information must be sent in cypher. By some mischance (possibly due to the arrival of new personnel) a message was sent by a Divisional Headquarters in September 1914 with this information in plain language, the place being a farm marked on all maps. Shortly afterwards a number of heavy shells fell upon the farm buildings, completely demolishing them and causing casualties ; it was by pure chance that certain senior officers who were present and who afterwards had a great influence on the progress of the war were not killed. Incidents such as these soon teach carefulness : they are avoidable, and all armies which employ wireless must possess a thorough system of training designed to prevent such indiscretions.

Apart from dramatic incidents arising from the successful interception of enemy messages, when time permits value is obtained from the accumulation of minor information obtained by routine observation.

In 1917 prolonged observation of the wireless signals from German aeroplanes enabled the British troops to understand that certain signals referred to certain groups of guns whose position was known. As a result of these observations it was possible to receive warning that these guns were about to commence a bombardment, and so when the known signal was heard, the German guns were bombarded at a moment when their crew were exposed, sometimes even before they had opened fire. Furthermore, the Royal Flying Corps were given warning that a German aeroplane was in the air for artillery observation in a certain area and were thus able to send aeroplanes to attack it.

Successful use of interception depends obviously on the receipt of the information sufficiently rapidly to give the Commander concerned time to act upon it. The message when received has to be sent to the General Staff, who may have to decipher it, re-write it, and transmit it to the responsible officer. In the case of a message of strategical importance, such as the Tannenberg incident quoted, the delay in the receipt of the information by the High Command may be much less than that required for counteraction, but in the case of a message of minor tactical importance, especially in mobile conditions, the delay in the receipt of a message by a junior Commander may often be so great as to make any counteraction too late.

It is therefore apparent that special observation stations can only work really efficiently if provided with good communication to the Army Staff.

Direction Finding.

There are several ways in which this can be usefully employed for army purposes : (1) By prolonged series of observations ; by two or more stations working under an efficient organization ; by this means it is possible to take a series of bearings upon enemy wireless stations, the average of which can be relied upon to be accurate within two degrees, and the intersections of these bearings, when plotted on a map, will indicate within a few hundred metres at most the position of the observed station. Usual observation from the air, or even from the ground, can therefore be directed upon the probable position. If not well concealed the situation of headquarters may thus be discovered and shelled or bombed.

(2) By observation from one D.F. station only, it is possible to detect the general direction of an enemy station, and a series of observations would detect movements it may make across the direction. This information might be of great value in detecting the presence of hostile forces in unexpected directions in mobile conditions.

(3) By recording the call signs and by taking cross bearings on all enemy stations heard, and plotting their positions on a map, it is possible to construct a schematic diagram of the enemy's wireless network. Although the accuracy of the observations may not be too good, such a diagram would give information as to the number of Brigades, Divisions, Corps, etc., involved and may indicate the approximate boundaries between their frontages. Such information is of considerable value in the planning of military operations.

There is no absolute method of avoiding observation by a direction finding station, except by not using wireless at all, but the advantages of wireless for its many qualities outweigh the risks of location by direction finding.

In recent years, as a result of the experience gained during the war of the importance of direction finding, mobile direction finding sets have been designed mounted in lorries or carts. These sets can take good bearings on small field sets using waves longer than 300 metres at a range of at least 15 miles. Even in mobile conditions therefore single D.F. sets can now be employed, although an elaborate system of detection cannot be set up under such conditions.

Interference.

Two types of interference are met with, deliberate and accidental. Deliberate interference with an enemy's wireless organization is a possibility. It is a two-edged sword however and invites retaliation ; furthermore it usually disturbs the communications of the user more than those of his intended victim.

Deliberate interference by a high power station was easy in the days of spark wireless telegraphy, but the advent of valves and continuous wave working has enabled receivers to be made so selective that the danger of such interference is minimized.

Deliberate interference by the field wireless sets of one belligerent with those of another is a more likely contingency but, needless to say, the interfering stations could not be used at the same time for their own legitimate communications, and therefore an army would have to sacrifice its own system of communications in order to interfere deliberately with that of its enemy. In the war from 1914 to 1918 deliberate interference of this kind was not a general practice. The possibility, indeed the certainty of adequate retaliation no doubt accounted for its absence on the grounds of " live and let live."

Accidental interference is another matter. Each belligerent endeavours to employ as many wavelengths as he needs, and there is no way of preventing both sides trying to use the same wavelength at the same time in the same locality, to their mutual disadvantage of course.

Accidental interference may also occur if one side tries to use more wireless stations in an area than the number of wavelengths will permit. A rough rule has been to allow twice the working range before the same wavelength is repeated. Thus stations on the front having a range of three miles can work satisfactorily provided that other stations of similar range do not use the same wavelength within six miles of them. Modern improvements in design and new wireless inventions tend continually to alter the technique of military wireless. It may well be that in the near future forward stations in the field and trench stations will be equipped with sets sending out waves only a few centimetres long, with horizontal aerials of a length of only a few centimetres, possibly provided with reflectors and ensuring communication with any point visible to the naked eye on which the reflector is set. Such sets have recently been developed ; they have many obvious advantages, and some disadvantages. Doubtless the practicability of the utilization of ultra short wave transmitters as quasi-optical beacons is being examined by competent military experts in all modern armies.

CHAPTER XI

WIRELESS IN WAR AT SEA

ON the invention of wireless telegraphy its first and most obvious application was to provide means whereby ships could maintain communication with the land and with each other.

In the British Navy great interest was at once shown in Marconi's invention, and in 1899 three ships, H.M.S. *Alexandria*, the flagship of Admiral Sir Compton Domville, H.M.S. *Juno*, with Captain Jackson in command, and H.M.S. *Europa*, were equipped with Marconi apparatus, so that its value could be ascertained during the Naval Manoeuvres. This was fully demonstrated, and it was clear to the Admiralty that wireless would profoundly affect the tactics of future naval warfare.

During the South African war the six wireless sets supplied to the Army were, in 1900, transferred to the British Naval Squadron blockading Delagoa Bay, and wireless proved its use in enabling ships to cooperate in concerted action although out of sight of each other. By the end of the year 42 ships in the British Navy had been equipped with wireless, and eight shore stations had been built. In 1905 over 80 ships had been equipped, and some fitted with long range receivers were able to receive from the Poldhu station in England even as far as Gibraltar. The possibility of the direct control of the Fleet from the Admiralty became evident, and with this end in view the Admiralty built a power station at Horsea, and another on the east coast at Cleethorpes. These stations were first equipped with 5 kw. spark sets but in 1909 were increased to 100 kw. capacity. In 1910 a similar station was built at Gibraltar, and in 1911 a 14 kw. station was erected at the Admiralty in Whitehall, and further similar stations at Aberdeen, Pembroke, and Ipswich. At the end of 1913 a highly organized naval wireless service had been established,

435 ships of the fleet had been equipped, and every ship could be in direct touch with the Admiralty, through one or other of the Naval land stations that had been erected. Wireless telegraphy had become the eyes and ears of the fleet at sea, and the days of independent action had definitely passed where an Admiral had to rely on his own judgment as to his operations, and on such information as his fast cruisers could obtain with regard to the enemy's movements or possible intentions. By the time the Great War broke out wireless had completely changed both the strategy and tactics of war at sea. Every fleet was in direct touch with the Admiralty, and every ship in every fleet in direct contact with each other. Concerted action could be taken by different fleets or squadrons out of sight of each other, and the direction of ships, friendly or hostile, could be ascertained. As the fleet grew and multiplied, collecting to itself flotillas of large and small vessels of every type for all kinds of services, they were all equipped with wireless, and the wireless organization was expanded with perfect smoothness to cope with its many duties.

The stations for the Imperial Wireless Communications had not been erected when war broke out, and there was always the danger that the vital cable connections of the Empire might be cut. The Germans had however built high power stations in their Colonies, and, although communication between them and Germany was at all times difficult, they rendered great service to Germany, in the first instance by warning all German shipping of the outbreak of war, not only with Russia and France but with England, and instructing German ships to make for the nearest neutral port.

The most important of these German Colonial stations was the high-power station in Togoland, erected at Kamina, about 100 miles from the coast. Togoland adjoined the British West African Gold Coast Colony in the Gulf of Guinea. The Kamina station was able to communicate direct with the Nauen station near Berlin, and it was the chief wireless centre in Africa for reception from Germany, and for the distribution of messages to the other German Colonies in East Africa, South-West Africa, the Cameroons, and Monrovia in Liberia, where three German-owned cables from South America terminated. Germany was forced to rely entirely upon wireless for communication with the outside world, the Kamina station being extensively used, when atmospheric conditions permitted, for relaying information and instructions to German Agents in South America. Furthermore, its range was extensive, it could cover a large portion of the South Atlantic Ocean, and thus send information to any German vessel in that area of the ocean.

Another powerful station had been erected by Germany at Windhuk, in German South-West Africa. On the east coast there was another station at Dar-es-Salaam. In the German Cameroons a small station had been erected at Duala. In the Pacific there were further German possessions and wireless stations, the principal ones being at Yap, Nairu, and Anguar. All these stations were actively or potentially dangerous to our shipping so long as any German raider was still free to operate. The importance of capturing or destroying these stations was appreciated at the Admiralty, and one by one they fell into our hands. The large expenditure incurred on their construction had however been amply justified by the services they rendered to Germany at the outset of the war. The British Navy cut all cable communications from Germany within four hours of the declaration of war, but through these wireless stations Germany was able to warn her Colonies, and to advise all German shipping to make for the nearest neutral port. A large number of German ships were thereby able to avoid capture.

By far the most important station was the Kamina station in Togoland, and this was the first to be destroyed. On the first day of the war Colonel Bryant with the Gold Coast Regiment proceeded to Lome, the chief German port, to summon the Colony to surrender, and on 7th August the German Governor abandoned Lome and agreed to surrender it. It was immediately occupied and used as a base for operations against Kamina. By 12th August Colonel Bryant had landed his force, and after severe difficulties he overcame the enemy resistance, whereupon, on 24th August, the Germans blew up the wireless station and surrendered. Thus the most important communication centre that Germany possessed was destroyed within three weeks of the outbreak of war.

The British Admiralty felt the need of a further expansion of its means of communication in every sea, and decided to build a network of strategic wireless stations at important points in the British Empire. Naval officers could not be spared from the Fleet or other services to erect these stations or to maintain and operate them, and the Author was therefore consulted by the Admiralty as to what could be done. As a result it was decided to erect Naval strategic stations of 30 kw. capacity at different points, viz. at St. Johns, Newfoundland ; Demerara, Bathurst in British Gambia, Port Nolloth on the South-West Coast of South Africa, Durban in Natal, Seychelles, and Mauritius, in the Indian Ocean, Aden, Ceylon, Singapore, and Hong Kong. It was also decided to build two 100 kw. stations at Ascension Island and at the Falkland Islands. The design, supply and construction of these stations were entrusted to the Marconi Company, and Marconi engineers and operators transferred to the R.N.V.R. were employed in their construction and operation until the end of the war. The stations were erected very rapidly, and by their means shipping on all the trade routes was adequately served.

Wireless in warfare not only provides a means whereby communication can be carried on between mobile forces, and enables instructions or information to be conveyed to ships at sea, but it also serves another most important function, namely, to ascertain the position or intercept the instructions or information sent out by enemy stations. This was well realized by the Admiralty, and early in the war the Marconi Company constructed for the Admiralty a number of direction finding stations around the coasts of Great Britain and Ireland, and others were built by the Post Office. The number of these stations was gradually increased as their uses were extended. Certain special direction finding stations were erected for constant watch on the German Fleet movements, whereas others were employed in locating the actual positions of Zeppelins or Submarines. Due to the work of Captain Round, M.C., the degree of accuracy of observation had become so remarkable that movements of the German ships in the harbours could be recorded, and the sensitivity of the direction finder receivers brought to such a very high pitch that the weak signals sent out by German warships in harbour in Kiel or Wilhelmshaven when talking to each other could be read.

Groups of direction finding stations were erected at various places on the English coast line, each group consisting of several stations to cover the different ranges of enemy wavelengths or different types of signals. While accurate bearings, often within $1\frac{1}{2}$ degrees, can be obtained with a direction finding station during the day, during the night the same degree of accuracy cannot be attained, the observed direction of the transmitting station often being as much as 30 degrees out of the true direction. It is not practicable to give a non-technical explanation of the reasons for these night errors, but on their account it was never safe to rely on the cross bearings obtained from two stations only ; three and preferably four different direction finding stations were generally used at night. Certain stations kept a never-ending watch on the signals transmitted from the various units of the German fleet, the operators, listening in day after day, learned to know the name of the ship sending by the nature of the signal, apart from the call letters, and whereas the Germans frequently changed their wavelength, the operators soon found that these changes were made by a regular rule, and time consequently was not lost in searching for the new wavelength. The importance of extreme accuracy in determining the positions of the German ships is self-evident, and Captain Round and his staff had brought this accuracy to such a high degree of perfection that the Admiralty placed great reliance upon the bearings given. The Grand Fleet was able to stay in harbour, with the full knowledge that any movement of the enemy fleet indicating that they were about to put to sea would instantly be detected. The Battle of Jutland was actually brought about by an observed motion of less than $1\frac{1}{2}$ degrees. How this came about had best be given in Admiral of the Fleet Sir Henry Jackson's own words : " I think I may say I trusted him (Captain Round) and his methods because we soon found them to be reliable. The trouble and intelligence of his staff reduced the errors to a

PLATE XI

[Photo by Spalding, Chelmsford

CAPT. H. G. ROUND, M.C.

[face p. 129

minimum, and where strategic movements were under consideration a few miles of error in the North Sea was of secondary importance. We have heard much about the use of direction finding for minor tactical movements of all arms, but this is a case of major strategical operation, which brought about the historical meeting of the British and German fleets at the Battle of Jutland on the 31st May 1916. I was First Sea Lord at the time, and so was responsible for the disposition of the Grand Fleet. I may incidentally mention that, in spite of other statements of which I have heard, its Commander-in-Chief (Lord Jellicoe) and I lived, so to speak, with the object of bringing off such a meeting. Our wireless direction finding stations under Captain Round kept careful and very intelligent watch on the positions of German ships using wireless and on the 30th May 1916 heard an unusual amount of wireless signals from one of the enemy's ships which they located at Wilhelmshaven. This was reported to me ; the time was a critical and anxious one in the war, and I had also some reasons for expecting that the German fleet might put out to sea during the week. Our fleet was ready at short notice, and had arranged unless otherwise prevented to put to sea on the following day for a sweep of the North Sea. But if the German Fleet got to sea first the chance of a meeting in waters not unfavourable to us was remote ; our object was to try to get to sea before or shortly after the Germans, and hitherto we had not succeeded in doing so. Later on in the afternoon it was reported to me that the German ship conducting the wireless had changed her position a few miles to the northward. Evidently she and her consorts had left the basins at Wilhelmshaven and had taken up a position in the Jade River ready to put to sea. This movement decided me to send our Grand Fleet to sea, and move towards the German Bight at once, and try to meet the German Fleet and bring it to action. This they did with their usual promptitude and the result was the famous Battle of Jutland, and it was indirectly brought about by the careful and accurate work of Captain Round and his staff, for which I hope they will accept my belated thanks and appreciation."

This incident is the supreme example of the use of direction

I

finding wireless to the Navy during the war, but many other important services were rendered. A chain of these stations was constructed on the look out for submarines. The German submarines were fitted with powerful spark stations, working on 400 metres, and when they sent any signals their location was immediately recorded. Search would be made for the submarine, and her course, if she transmitted on several different occasions, could be determined and shipping warned; doubtless many ships were saved in consequence.

Another important service rendered was the location of Zeppelins en route to raid England or returning from a raid. The German Navy directed the Zeppelins by direction finding from land stations. The Zeppelin would send out signals at constant intervals, and the German land stations would take the bearings of the signals and telegraph back to the Zeppelin her position. The German direction finding stations, unlike the British, were not favourably located, owing to the configuration of their frontier, to obtain a good base line and thus a wide angle for accurate cross bearings, and on several occasions their observations were most inaccurate. The importance and value of direction finding stations to the British Navy is referred to in Admiral Scheers' book, *Germany's High Sea Fleet in the World War*, from which the following quotation is taken :—

> " The English received the news of our movements through their directional wireless, which they already had in use but which were only introduced by us at a much later period . . . the stretch of the English east coast is very favourable for the erection of these direction stations. In possessing them the English had a great advantage in the conduct of the war as they were able to obtain quite accurate information as to the locality of the enemy as soon as any wireless signals were sent by him. In the case of a large fleet, where separate units are stationed far apart and communication between them is essential, an absolute cessation of wireless intercourse would be fatal to any enterprise."

It is interesting to speculate as to what form the war would have taken had wireless never been invented. The advantages that wireless conferred during the war were greater to the Allies than to the Germans.

In land warfare aircraft cooperation with the artillery

would have been very difficult, but this applies equally to both sides. In naval warfare however the situation would have been altered profoundly in favour of the Germans. The British Fleet would have had to keep constantly at sea, any movement of the enemy ships from their base could only be known many hours afterwards, and then only by a carrier pigeon service or by a chain of cruisers relaying visual signals from one to the other. Far greater freedom of action would have been automatically available for the German Fleet, and cooperation between squadrons of fleets out of sight of each other would have been impossible. As regards the submarine campaign it is probable that it would have been successful. There would have been no means of locating their position nor of issuing warning signals to merchant ships, nor would it be known when a ship was being attacked, nor where.

Chapter XII

WIRELESS IN WAR IN THE AIR

THE use of wireless in aeroplanes is essentially a war development. At the beginning of the war there were only four squadrons of the Royal Flying Corps in France, and the machines then used were slow and incapable of flying at a great height. They were not provided with machine guns and the only means available for signalling from an aeroplane were by Verey lights or flags. It was soon realized by the High Command that the aeroplane could furnish accurate information of the enemy's position or movements, but the delay in returning to report under mobile conditions of warfare frequently prevented counter action being taken until too late. . The need for wireless communication from aeroplane to ground was obvious, but the weight of wireless transmitters was a serious obstacle. Previous to the war wireless had been used successfully from and to " airships " for observation purposes. It was known therefore that it was possible to signal from an aircraft by wireless. In 1907 the first wireless experiments were carried out by Lieut. C. J. Aston, R.E., in a captive balloon and in 1908 Lieut. Aston in a balloon, in which receiving apparatus had been installed, received good signals when 20 miles from the ground transmitting station : later in the year good results were obtained in transmitting from a balloon. In 1909 Capt. H. P. T. Lefroy, R.E., was in charge of all wireless experimental work in the Army. When the Army Airship the " Beta " was built he equipped the ship with wireless apparatus, and in 1911 he was able to transmit successfully from the ship up to distances of 30 miles. In 1912 Capt. Lefroy designed a transmitting set for use in aeroplanes. In June 1912 Commander Samson on a Short seaplane succeeded in sending messages up to distances of 10 miles.

In August 1912 during the Army manoeuvres airships

fitted with wireless were employed on observation, and the signals from the " Gamma " were received at 35 miles. General Grierson, who commanded one side, stated : " The impression left upon my mind is that their use has revolution-ized the art of war. . . . The airship was of more use to me than the aeroplanes as, being fitted with wireless telegraphy, I received messages in a continuous stream, and immediately after the observations had been made." Considerable progress was made during the two years before the war in experiments on communication from and to aircraft, and signals were read from airships up to distances of 130 miles. By the time war broke out wireless had been fitted to sixteen aeroplanes and two airships. Very little was however known, outside of the services, of the progress that had been made in aircraft wireless during the years preceding the war. The Navy had perhaps devoted more attention to this development, since the responsibility of the coastal defence of England was theirs, and the necessity of the air patrols keeping in touch with the Navy at considerable distances was obvious. There was how-ever a close liaison between the Navy and the Royal Flying Corps during the period of development, and, although their individual needs and problems differed in many respects, this liaison helped each service to make substantial progress in all matters connected with aircraft. Several incidents prior to the war indicated the potential value of wireless to aircraft and for war purposes. In one instance a Navy seaplane fitted with wireless kept in communication with the coastal re-ceiving stations throughout its flight for a distance of 35 miles. During the Naval manoeuvres of 1913 Commander Samson, scouting off the east coast, was forced to come down due to engine failure, but his messages by wireless located her and the seaplane was thereby found.

During the Army manoeuvres of the same year the two airships, " Delta " and " Eta," gave useful service in observa-tion and were able to exchange messages 100 miles apart. In June 1914 two wireless officers who did much to develop wireless for aeroplane use, Lieuts. D. S. Lewis and B. T. James, both of whom were killed during the war, were able to keep in communication when on a long flight flying 10 miles apart.

At the time war broke out a wireless section had been formed in the Royal Flying Corps and this section was attached to No. 4 Squadron, but in September 1914 a Headquarters Wireless Unit, under the command of Major Musgrave, was formed. In December the unit was enlarged and became No. 9 Squadron, stationed at Headquarters in France ; before the end of the year the demands for wireless equipped machines had become so insistent that flights from this Squadron had to be allotted to each of the two wings. As the number of wings grew so did the call for wireless sets, and eventually all artillery squadrons were equipped with wireless apparatus, the equipping of the aeroplanes becoming the duty of the Aircraft Park.

When trench warfare began artillery officers were taken up daily by aeroplanes to observe the positions of hostile batteries on the maps, so that counter battery fire could be undertaken. On the Aisne wireless was used for the first time for artillery observation, but for the most part other methods of signalling had to be' used, as the number of machines fitted with wireless were few, but when once the artillery had experienced the greater accuracy and the speed with which information could be sent from the aeroplane by wireless there was a constant demand for the use of the wireless machines.

Soon the importance of wireless observation was fully appreciated, and every effort was made to design a light and effective transmitter. Early in 1915 a consignment of improved transmitters and rather clumsy ground receivers for use at batteries was delivered in France and they were employed on artillery cooperation work. Every Battery Commander, who had experience of the observation work carried out by a wireless fitted aeroplane, was dissatisfied with any other form of observation and so the demand quickly grew for more and more wireless machines, and it was clear that wireless from the air was going to play a very important part in the war. Not only was it necessary to supply an ever-increasing number of wireless sets, but it was also essential to have the necessary technical personnel to look after them and wireless operators at each battery to read the signals. Schools for wireless officers and operators were established in England, and Commissions in the R.F.C. were granted to a number of wireless engineers from the Marconi Company and other concerns who had the necessary technical knowledge. Meanwhile those responsible for the technical design of the apparatus were busily engaged in re-modelling the sets for use in France ; the weights and sizes of the sets were greatly reduced, and they were made more reliable in every way. Improvements and new devices were made from time to time in design and in technical organization throughout the years of the war, until finally at the end of the war there were no less than 600 aeroplanes fitted with wireless apparatus at the Front and over 100 ground stations, with more than 1800 wireless operators.

There were two principal duties assigned to the artillery cooperation machines, (1) the carrying out of pre-arranged shoots on selected hostile gun positions or other targets, by one or more of our batteries, and (2) patrolling the lines on the look-out for flashes from hostile guns in action. In the latter case the flashes were reported by wireless and the point on the map square of the hostile battery located, and our guns covering that particular area opened up in order to neutralize or silence the hostile fire.

In the case of a pre-arranged shoot on an enemy battery the aeroplane would fly between the battery and the target for a flight generally lasting three hours. When one hostile gun had been put out of action by a direct hit the plane would signal to the battery accordingly, and the guns would be switched on to the next gun or to another hostile battery. The signals directing artillery fire consisted of code letters ; the method used was what is known as the clock code. The target was taken as the centre of a clock and imaginary con-centric circles were drawn around it at 10, 25, 50, 100, 200, 300, 400 and 500 yards. These lines were lettered Y Z A B C D E F respectively. Twelve o'clock was always taken as true north from the centre of the circle, that is to say the target. The observer noticed the fall of the shell with refer-ence to the imaginary lines and clock hours, and would signal down his observation thus, B9 C4 Z10 Z3 Y4 OK, these observations showing that the ranging shells were gradually getting nearer and nearer to the target until a direct hit took place. Messages from the battery, squadron, or other ground station, were signalled to the aeroplane by means of strips of white American cloth which were laid out on the ground to form the letters of a code.

It must be remembered that except in special cases, where shoots were being carried out by long range Naval guns, the distance of the aeroplane from the guns was never more than the range of the gun to the target. The plane flew backwards and forwards in two intersecting loops, watching for the fall of the shell when flying towards the target and giving the corrections when flying towards the battery. At the time of the Battle of the Aisne the machines flew at a low height, but as the anti-aircraft guns improved in accuracy and range, the observation aeroplanes were forced to fly higher and higher.

The chief duties of the artillery cooperation aeroplanes were to carry out shoots with batteries on known targets, and to report positions of new or active batteries by observing the flash from their guns. In the possibility of a successful break through the German lines, resulting in open warfare, it was realized that when the batteries moved forward they would have to register on new and unknown targets, and there would be difficulties in arranging individual shoots with definite batteries. A system of zone calls was therefore devised due to Major Ludlow Hewitt. The map squares of the front and back areas were each divided into four zones, based on the lettered square of the map, the four zones being lettered for instance E, F, G, K, each covering an area of 3000 yards square. The call sent down was composed of the map square letter followed by the zone letter. The observer transmitted any information of troops or hostile batteries he saw, prefacing his message with the zone call in which the target was seen. Batteries capable of covering that zone, under the Group Artillery Commander's instructions, would thereupon concentrate their fire on the position indicated.

In the early days of artillery cooperation the wireless officer of the R.F.C. Squadron, responsible for the successful operation of the wireless apparatus on the plane and the reception of the signals at the battery, endeavoured to get the utmost energy from the wireless transmitter in order to overcome interference from the wireless signals from an aeroplane working a shoot from an adjacent squadron. It was soon found that this only increased mutual interference, whereas by reducing the power of each transmitter to what was actually necessary to give reasonably good signals at the battery, and by the very careful tuning of the transmitter and aerial, interference was greatly reduced, and it was possible to increase the number of aeroplanes on each Corps front doing simultaneous shoots. The rapid increase in the number of squadrons fitted with wireless, and the ever-increasing concentration of artillery along the Front, rendered it necessary to crowd in as many machines as possible without interfering with each other's signals. This was further facilitated by the careful selection of wavelengths employed, and by the introduction of the " Clapper break," by which means it was possible to give wireless transmitters distinctive notes.

Before the Somme the maximum number of wireless aeroplanes that could be used simultaneously was one for every two thousand yards ; by the spring of 1917 this was reduced to one per thousand yards, and at the time of the Armistice one plane could be used for every four hundred yards of front.

A good example of what could be done was demonstrated in the Battle of Messines on 7th June 1917. No less than 20 machines were working at one time on a 4-mile front. The success of this battle was due to a large degree to the effective work of the R.F.C. in directing gun-fire on hostile positions. Some 70 hostile batteries were directing a flanking fire from the north of the salient ; the whole of this German artillery was silenced by our artillery in two hours, directed on the German batteries by flash spotting aeroplanes reporting the positions of the enemy guns by wireless. The high pitch of efficiency of artillery cooperation can be illustrated by a sample month's work :—

Total number of shoots carried out . .	1,562
Total number of calls received from flash spotting aeroplanes	74,201
Percentage received to those missed . .	86
Total failures due to breakdown of wireless gear in plane or at battery . . .	11

The ordinary method for artillery cooperation could not be carried out effectively in the case of long range high velocity guns firing at distant targets. The range of 12-inch and 9·2-inch guns often required the aeroplane to fly some 10 to 15 miles over the lines. It was therefore necessary to employ a more powerful transmitter, and to instal a receiver in order to avoid the necessity of machines having to return to the vicinity of the battery to receive messages by visual signalling. The aeroplanes so equipped were able to carry on " two way " communication over the hostile target.

Before giving details of the other developments of wireless in the R.F.C. it may be of interest to refer to the organization which dealt with the large amount of material and maintained the wireless equipment in the necessary state of efficiency. Every squadron had two wireless officers, under the Wing Wireless Officer, who in turn was responsible to the Brigade Officer. The Squadron Wireless Officer was responsible for the wireless equipment, not only on the aeroplanes of the squadron, but also for the wireless apparatus at each of the batteries situated in the area wherein his squadron cooperated with the artillery. He was also responsible for the welfare and equipment of the operators at the batteries. It was found that the efficiency of the system depended very largely on the way the operators were handled and their needs quickly attended to. Every Brigade of Siege and Heavy Artillery and every Divisional Artillery Headquarters had one R.F.C. Patrol Corporal attached. These Corporals patrolled the ground stations at the batteries in their particular areas. They were responsible for seeing that each receiving station was in an efficient condition and that the operators had all they required in the way of apparatus, clothing, etc. In addition to the ground stations at the batteries, checking stations were located at Divisional, Brigade and Corps Artillery Headquarters ; the stations located at Squadron and Advanced Squadron Headquarters were also employed for checking signals and testing the equipment for aeroplanes.

The central wireless stations, established near the Headquarters of the Corps Artillery in each area, were for the purpose of minimising errors and locating the cause of missed calls. The Central Station was equipped with several aerials and receivers and listened in to all shoots. If communication broke down between plane and battery, the observer could call up the Central station, which, if necessary, could carry out the shoot with the battery.

Throughout the war the system of wireless used on aeroplanes for cooperation with the artillery was the spark system and all messages were by telegraph. Late in 1917 the development of the wireless transmitting valve had made substantial progress, and an extremely light and efficient continuous wave transmitter was produced which gave a range of about 100 miles from aeroplane to ground. These were installed in a number of night-bombing squadrons, and machines so fitted were able to report direct to Squadron Headquarters any information gleaned. The enemy up to the time of the Armistice had not been able to design a continuous wave transmitter for use in the air. This was borne out by the capture of a document stating that the English had been able to construct a continuous wave transmitter for use in aeroplanes, and offering large rewards for the salving of any portions of the wireless apparatus from a night bombing machine brought down behind their lines.

Continuous waves were also extensively employed before the end of the war at ground stations. All Squadrons, Wings, Brigades and Headquarters were linked up by this method as an alternative to land lines, and this proved of great use from the time of the commencement of the rapid advance in 1918 until the occupation of Cologne.

The use of wireless telegraphy in the R.F.C. during the period of the war was necessary only because wireless telephony had not at that time been sufficiently developed for aircraft purposes. The use of Morse code was slow and necessitated the pilot and observer learning how to use it among the many other details of their training. Efforts were made to develop satisfactory telephone apparatus but the difficulties to be surmounted were great. The apparatus to be of value would have to be light, reliable, easily operated and capable of being fitted in any type of machine. For communication between machines it must have a range of at least two miles, and with the ground 20 miles. Speech would have to be of good quality, and understandable above the noise of the engines. If these difficulties could be overcome there would be valuable services which telephony could render in aerial warfare. The Leader could control each machine in his formation. Leaders of separate formations could speak to each other and arrange combined evolutions, machines could speak direct to the ground, and the ground could speak to the leaders of one or more formations for the purpose of immediate concentration at any point.

A telephone transmitter was evolved in 1915 which gave successful results up to a range of 20 miles from aeroplane to ground, and in 1916 a wireless telephone receiver was designed and tried out in the air, but owing to the early stage in the advancement of valve design at that date, the set had to be provided with numerous adjusting gear and required the services of a skilled operator, so that it was unsuitable for war service. It was not until 1917 that a practical wireless telephone set for aeroplanes was evolved. This set, while a great advance on previous designs, still required a certain amount of experience before the pilot could handle it, so schools were set up to train them, and Squadrons were equipped in 1918, both for home defence and for overseas.

The immediate needs of the war gave a great impetus to wireless design. Knowledge was gained which in times of peace might have taken years to acquire. The experiences of the war and the failings or insufficiency of the apparatus then used have brought about a great advancement in the design of wireless aircraft apparatus. Modern designs embrace types of both telegraph and telephone receivers for every military purpose, and now it is possible not only to use telephony for communication between planes but to communicate to and from planes over distances of thousands of miles. Furthermore, air stations in the remotest parts of the British Empire can now communicate direct with the R.A.F. Headquarters in London and the problem of Air Force communications has thereby been simplified. Although such radical changes have taken place since the war, there is no doubt that by rendering it possible to communicate rapidly from an aeroplane to the ground the artillery were able to silence many hundreds of hostile guns, which otherwise would have been active, and wireless therefore in its many activities played a large part in the final result.

Chapter XIII

WIRELESS TO THE RESCUE AT SEA

THE earliest application of wireless was and is still its most important one, namely the " Safety of Life and Property at Sea." There was no means available previous to the invention of wireless of appealing for help from other vessels out of sight, from a ship in distress, and the crew and passengers had to take to the boats, trusting that sooner or later they might be seen by some passing vessel. Generally days, sometimes weeks, passed before the boats were seen. How many cases are there when ships have been posted as lost and no trace ever found of ship, passengers or crew again, when had wireless been installed help would have been available and the lives of some at least saved? Take the case of the *Waratah*, on her voyage from Australia to England in 1909. The *Waratah* put into the port of Durban in Natal. The author happened to be present at the docks when she sailed, never to be seen again. There was a strong gale blowing but no one dreamt that we were seeing her for the last time. Whatever disaster occurred will never be known, no wreckage or trace of her was ever found. At the time there was no wireless coastal station in Natal, and her loss is one of the many sea disasters that wireless, now that it is compulsory at sea, might have explained, although perhaps not have averted.

It is generally appreciated that the natural function of wireless is to " broadcast " a signal, although the word broadcast in modern times serves to denote a popular service of music, entertainment, news, and instruction, to all who have wireless receivers tuned in to the wavelength of the transmitting station.

When a transmitting station creates a disturbance in the ether, waves travel out from the transmitting aerial in all directions, just in the same way as when you throw a stone

into a pond circular waves travel out from where the stone
fell. One of the main problems in wireless commercial communication has been to direct the energy from the transmitting aerial in such a way that the waves emitted would
be concentrated in the required direction, but in the case of
marine services, for communication between ship and ship
and ship to shore, the principle of broadcasting is essential.
Those who listen in to broadcast programmes know the importance of tuning. Those who laid down the rules for Safety
of Life at Sea also appreciated the importance of the receivers
on every ship being responsive to one definite selected wavelength, 600 metres, on which calls of distress are sent out.
However elaborate the wireless equipment on a ship may
be, whether carrying means for telephony to the shore, high
speed commercial service equipment, or means for reception
of picture telegraphy, all such ships must also be equipped
with apparatus for transmitting on 600 metres wave and also
be provided with spark emergency apparatus in event of
accident, to send out distress calls on the wavelength of
600 metres.

Under International regulations all ships fitted with wireless are required to listen at regular intervals for distress calls,
S.O.S., or warning signals T.T.T. In British ships all ordinary
wireless work is suspended for three minutes at quarter past
and quarter to each hour Greenwich time. During these
times the British operators on all ships in every ocean listen
simultaneously for any distress or warning call. Distress
calls might possibly be missed at other times but this regulation ensures that every distress call sent at the official
times will be received by some ships within the range of the
distressed vessel. There is no danger nowadays that this
insistent distress call S.O.S.—three dots three dashes three
dots—will be missed ; all operators are always, perhaps un-
consciously, listening for it, and the signal is so distinctive
to an operator, it is like calling him by his name, that even
a weak S.O.S. would be heard.

On the formation of the first wireless commercial Company,
The Wireless Telegraph and Signal Company Limited, its
main ambition was to instal wireless on the Lighthouses and
Lightships around the coasts of Great Britain. In 1898

Trinity House, who control this service around the English coast, installed wireless on the East Goodwin Lightship and the shore, for purposes of test and investigation as to the practical utility of wireless. The first use of wireless to a ship was in January 1899, when a heavy sea struck the East Goodwin Lightship, carrying away part of her bulwarks ; the mishap was reported to Trinity House. Two months later the s.s. *R. F. Mathews* ran into the East Goodwin Lightship ; the accident was at once reported by wireless and lifeboats were immediately sent to the rescue of the crew. From the publicity given to this incident attention was at once drawn to the services that wireless might render to the safety of ships at sea, and Shipping Companies became interested in installing wireless on the vessels they operated. From this date the number of ships equipped with wireless rapidly increased, until the time came when international legislation made wireless compulsory on all ships over a certain tonnage. At the present moment (1932) there are more than 15,000 ships equipped with wireless telegraphy, and of these nearly 4000 are British.

As the number of ships equipped with wireless grew the occasions when wireless rendered valuable assistance to shipping increased in number. We will give a few early instances, each of which emphasised the importance of wireless to shipping, and speeded up the rate at which shipping was equipped with wireless.

On 1st January 1901 the Channel steamer the *Princess Clementine,* reported that the barque *Madeira* of Stockholm was waterlogged on Ratel Bank. A tug was promptly despatched and she was saved. On 19th January the same ship, the *Princess Clementine,* ran ashore at Mariakerke during a fog. News of the accident was reported by wireless and the ship was saved. In December 1903 the Red Star liner *Kroonland* was disabled 130 miles from the Fastnet and reported the trouble she was in to the wireless station at Crookhaven in Ireland and assistance was sent to her. In 1904 accidents to the s.s. *New York* and s.s. *Friesland* were reported by wireless. In January 1909 an accident occurred which, but for the help of wireless, would have been a serious disaster. The s.s. *Republic* was rammed by the s.s. *Florida* and eventually sank. A broadcast appeal for help was at once sent out by the operator, Jack Binns, whose name became widely known owing to the publicity given to this event and to the calm manner in which he dealt with the emergency. He sent out distress calls and ships rushed to the rescue with the result that all the passengers and crew were saved before the *Republic* plunged to the depths of the ocean. In the same year on 10th June the s.s. *Slavonia* ran ashore on the Azores, when all her passengers and crew were rescued from the wreck, due to assistance summoned by wireless. In 1911 H.M.S. *Cornwall* ran ashore on Cape Sable (N.S.) and reported her trouble by wireless and was rescued. The same year the Donaldson liner s.s. *Saturnia* struck an icebreg 175 miles east of Belle Isle Straits ; assistance was sent to her on receipt of her wireless call for help and she was successfully brought to port. Again in the same year the P. & O. liner *Delhi* with the Duke and Duchess of Fife on board reported she was in distress off Cape Spartel ; assistance was sent and everbody safely landed.

On 14th April 1912 occurred one of the great maritime disasters. The new White Star liner *Titanic*, the largest and most perfectly equipped vessel of her day, was on her maiden voyage to New York. At 11.40 p.m. she suddenly struck an iceberg. She had been warned by wireless that there was plenty of ice about but continued to travel at twenty-one knots. When she struck the ice the blow sliced open a wound 300 feet long, but the blow gave so slight a shock that the extent of the disaster was not at once appreciated. At 12.15 Phillips, the Marconi operator, started sending out the distress call C.Q.D. (this was the original distress call before the S.O.S. signal was universally adopted). He followed this call with the demand " Come at once struck berg Lat. 41° 46' N., Long. 50° 14' W. advise Captain," at 12.42 he sent out the C.Q.D. and S.O.S. call. These calls were received by a number of ships, the *Carpathia*, *Frankfurt*, *Caronia*, *Virginian*, *Olympic*, *Birma* and *Baltic*, and they continued until 2.17 a.m. when the signals stopped and the *Titanic* sank, with 1503 aboard and 703 scantily clothed men, women and children in the boats.

K

Four hours later the *Carpathia*, having received the call when 70 miles away, arrived on the spot and saw some floating wreckage ; a few minutes later some of the ship's boats were sighted and their occupants rescued. Phillips, the operator, stayed at his post. When told by the Captain he could do no further good he returned to his cabin and put on the telephones to listen to the remarks of ships coming to the rescue. He died, an example of sacrifice to duty and an inspiration to the service to which he belonged. His assistant McBride stayed with him to the end and was picked up in the sea after about an hour and a half. To him also the admiration of his colleagues in the Marconi Company is likewise extended. The greatest tragedy in this terrible disaster is that this great loss of life might have been avoided. In those days it was not compulsory for a ship to keep a continuous wireless watch and many ships only carried one operator. There was a ship equipped with a wireless actually in sight of the *Titanic* at the time of the disaster, the *Californian*. She carried only one operator : at 10.30 the *Californian* had met the ice that caused the disaster and stopped dead. Half an hour later the lights of another ship were seen. About the same time the operator of the *Californian* got in touch with Phillips on the *Titanic*, but the latter was busy with traffic and asked him to keep off the ether. The *Californian* officers did not realize that the lights of the steamer they could see was the *Titanic*, and when she ceased to proceed they assumed that she had stopped as they had on account of the field of ice. The *Californian* operator had retired to bed, there was no other operator on board, no one on the *Californian* had any idea that the *Titanic* was in trouble and so, although only about 8 miles away, was blind to the tragedy that was being enacted. The means of salvation were available on the *Californian*, but the operator had been on duty from the early hours of the morning until 11 p.m. and without him the ship was deaf to all calls. It was not his fault, the system was to blame. Wireless was compulsory on ships of a certain size, but a continuous wireless watch was not. The *Titanic* disaster brought about a revision and stiffening up of regulations, not only as regards wireless, but also in respect of the supply of an adequate number of lifeboats. Shortly after this disaster the Board of Trade in England passed a regulation that all ships carrying more than a certain minimum number of passengers must carry sufficient wireless operators to keep a continuous watch.

In November 1912 the s.s. *Oravia* struck a rock on the Falkland Islands in the South Atlantic ; her wireless calls were heard and passengers and mails were saved before the vessel was lost. In the autumn of 1913 another sea drama occurred. On 10th October the s.s. *Volturno*, when 1000 miles west of Ireland, burst into flames and those on board were faced with the choice of death by drowning or burning. The distress call S.O.S. was at once sent forth giving the ship's position. The *Volturno* was an emigrant ship of only 3600 tons ; she was better equipped than the *Titanic* from the point of view of the safety of passengers and crew. There was an ample supply of boats and she carried two wireless operators, keeping a constant night and day watch. The Volturno had encountered a succession of gales since she left Rotterdam and on the 9th October a severe gale was blowing. Suddenly she burst into fire, explosions followed, and within five minutes of the first indication of fire the hatches had blown off and flames were rising as high as the top of the foremast. The ship was turned before the wind to keep the flames from spreading aft. Explosion followed explosion and it was clear that the ship was doomed. Boats were launched but all who attempted to get away in boats were lost in the raging seas. Wireless calls of distress had been sent out and ships hurried to her assistance. Suddenly another fire burst out in her coal bunkers, and cut off her supply of fuel and the situation of her passengers and crew became more desperate than ever. The rescuing ships began to arrive, some from one bearing some from another, until the *Volturno* was surrounded with a ring of vessels all wanting to help, but unable to on account of the raging seas. The Cunard liner *Carmania* was the first to arrive, followed by the German liners *Seydlitz* and *Grosser Kurfürst*. Later on came the *Kroonland*, *La Touraine*, *Devonian* and *Minneapolis*. Twelve answered the S.O.S. call. The last to arrive was an oil tanker the

Narrangansett and this vessel, by discharging oil on the seas, made it eventually possible to launch boats and rescue the remaining passengers and crew. 520 were saved out of a total of 654. The major loss of life was due to the swamping of the *Volturno's* boats in the heavy seas when the fire first broke out, but had it not been for wireless all would certainly have perished.

In May 1914 occurred another terrible marine disaster which, because of its sheer wantonness, sent a shock throughout the world. The *Empress of Ireland* was struck amidships by a Norwegian collier, the s.s. *Storstad*, in calm water in the Gulf of St. Lawrence. Both ships had observed each other's lights, each steamer was showing green to green, and there was no risk of collision, but fog suddenly descended while the course of the *Empress of Ireland* was being changed and the lights of the *Empress of Ireland* were misinterpreted by the Norwegian vessel with the result that the liner was struck and sank in fifteen minutes. Immediately S.O.S. signals were sent out. The wireless operator, without waiting for orders sent out the distress call, telling all who were listening in to stand by. He did this to ensure that the ether would be clear for his message when the Captain gave it him. The Chief Officer then told him to send out the S.O.S., which was received at a land station, Father Point, and tugs were rushed to the spot where the *Empress of Ireland* had sunk. Out of 1417 passengers and crew 217 passengers and 248 of the crew only were saved. The suddenness of the disaster prevented the rescue of more lives. The sea was calm, the waters sheltered, no one could have foreseen the possibility of such a catastrophe, but had it not been for the wireless distress call few if any of the voyagers would have been saved.

There are a number of other cases that might be cited of the saving of life at sea through the medium of wireless. For those who wish to have fuller particulars of these marine disasters I can recommend a book called *S.O.S. and T.T.T.*, by Mr. Bennet Copplestone. The few incidents given serve to show the enormous importance of wireless for minimising the risks to shipping. Since wireless was first installed on a ship in 1898 over 11,000 lives and much valuable property have been saved through the agency of wireless in major marine disasters during times of peace, apart from the thousands of lives saved at sea during the Great War. It is not possible to estimate the total number of lives which have been saved from both large and small ships, owing to the difficulty of gathering records from all parts of the world in those cases where only a small number of persons are concerned, but it must be very considerably more than the above figure. Wireless may also claim credit for the safety of lives and ships which avoid dangers due to wireless warnings, as well as for those lives actually saved in cases where the ship has foundered.

During the Great War the value of wireless to the Merchant Marine and indeed all shipping was incalculable. Many lives were lost at sea due to attacks by submarines, but imagine the consequences to the mercantile fleet from the submarine campaign if there had been no means on board ship to call for help and to indicate to the Navy the whereabouts of the hostile craft. Without the risk of their presence being reported the submarines would have had great freedom of action, and it is probable that the number of ships sunk by submarine action under such conditions would have brought about a different ending to the war. A large number of wireless operators lost their lives as a result of submarine attacks. No less than 348 of the 6000 operators in the employment of the Marconi International Marine Communication Company were killed as a result of submarine attacks, while many others serving in the Royal Navy or auxiliary forces shared a similar fate.

Modern developments in marine wireless, the use of the direction finder and the automatic alarm—a mechanical device which responds only to a distress call, and rings an alarm bell when such a signal is received—the employment of the echo meter for soundings, and the constant improvements in all matters which help to the security of ships at sea may, we hope, ensure that serious maritime disasters will become less and less frequent in the future and that when they do unavoidably occur they will be accompanied by little loss of life.

Chapter XIV

WIRELESS MARINE COMMUNICATION

WIRELESS has been recognized from its earliest days as particularly fitted to serve the needs of ships at sea, and marine communication was the first form of wireless telegraphy to be developed on a commercial basis. It still remains the most important application of wireless, since communication with ships at sea can be effected in no other manner.

In addition to the useful service it renders in daily communication between ship and shore and ship and ship, and the frequent epic part it has played in saving life and property at sea, it is now an essential aid to navigation and its scope has been largely widened in other directions. The development of the modern wireless telegraph and telephone installations has increased the facilities of communication. Direction finders, beacon stations, and fog guns, have minimized the risks to shipping and facilitated navigation ; again the provision of music players and band repeaters contributes to the amusement and entertainment of passengers and crew, while the publication of news bulletins provides them with a constant link with the outside world. The principal method of communication with ships is by telegraphy, and modern wireless apparatus for ships enables messages to be sent over very long distances. International legislation from time to time has laid down regulations for facilitating marine communication, and ensuring that ship services shall be kept up to date with modern progress in so far as it is commercially practicable.

Gradually the use of the old spark system is being discontinued except for distress calls, for which spark transmitters provide the best form of emergency apparatus, due to the strident nature of the signal emitted, and regulations have been imposed forbidding the installation of any new spark transmitter of greater power than 300 watts input.

The equipment of ships with modern valve transmitters is thus steadily progressing, and while it will be some years before the majority of ships are so fitted, the cause of complaint by the public living near the coast of interference from ships' spark sets with broadcast programmes will gradually disappear. Valve transmitters are now carried by all the more important passenger ships, which are consequently enabled to keep in touch with land throughout their voyages. The oceans are thus covered by a wireless network, which is not only invaluable as a life saving medium but also facilitates the handling of messages on behalf of passengers and in connection with the business of ships at sea.

The introduction of short wave wireless for very long distance communication between fixed stations naturally attracted the attention of those interested in marine communication. Certain ships were equipped with suitable short wave sets and satisfactory results were obtained at great distances. The Washington Conference of 1927 therefore, realizing the need for this type of service, allocated several bands of wavelengths in the short wave spectrum for mobile services, and a steadily increasing number of ships are being equipped with short wave transmitters and receivers.

Wireless direction finding on board ship is of great importance, and the reliance that can be placed on its accuracy in assisting navigation is responsible for the increased use of direction finders on board ship and the erection of wireless beacon stations around the coasts. More than 4000 ships are now fitted with direction finders, or about one-quarter of the total number of ships carrying wireless. In Great Britain and Ireland the Corporation of Trinity House and other coastal authorities have erected a series of Marconi beacon transmitters, as an aid to navigation in British waters, while a large number of similar transmitters have been erected by other Governments on their sea board littorals. There are now more than 200 automatic wireless beacon stations in operation and others are being erected. Fifteen are in operation around the coasts of Great Britain and Ireland, apart from those in process of construction.

Beacon stations are automatic in operation, being controlled by a master clock which starts and stops the transmitter at regular intervals. A pre-arranged signal is transmitted at definite times and ships fitted with wireless direction finders are thus able to fix their position by a series of bearings which they can take at will. The beacon station is analogous to a lighthouse sending definitely timed flashes by which navigators can fix their positions, but the wireless beacon has the advantage of being as efficient and reliable in foggy weather as in clear weather conditions. All ships fitted with direction finders within the range of the beacon station can take bearings simultaneously without delay or interference with one another, regardless of poor visibility or bad weather conditions.

An automatic wireless beacon can be installed at any lighthouse at reasonable cost and, no additional staff being required, the expense of maintenance is small. Such an installation uses only a fraction of the power of a sound fog signal and its signals effectively cover an area about 300 times as great. With modern equipments reliable bearings can be obtained from wireless beacon stations at distances up to 100 miles, which is more than sufficient for navigational purposes.

Another development as an aid to navigation has been the introduction of the Rotating Beacon. This apparatus enables ships or aircraft, fitted with ordinary wireless receivers, to obtain their bearings from the beacon with sufficient accuracy for navigation purposes. The Rotating Beacon meets an important need, it enables the small ship to avoid the cost of installing and operating a ship direction finding apparatus and, in the case of aircraft, to avoid the extra weight of the aircraft direction finder, and the difficulties and limitations that still exist in the equipment of direction finders on aeroplanes. Before leaving the subject of direction finding it may not be out of place to deal with the advantages, gained by its equipment, to fishing trawlers.

Whilst in times of emergency the direction finder may be of particular value in safeguarding the lives of the crew and the property of the owners, it is the normal every-day service which it renders that makes it appeal most particularly to trawler owners and skippers. Trawlers so fitted are able to take frequent bearings of other ships, either for safe navigation in foggy weather, or, as is most frequently the case in the fishing industry, to take bearings of ships belonging to the same owners, which have reported by wireless that they are on a good fishing ground. A vessel can report in code to her sister ships that she is in waters where fish are plentiful, and the other trawlers can then use their direction finders to determine the bearing and avoid waste of time in getting to the ground indicated. One of the most dramatic instances of the value of wireless direction finders on board trawlers was contained in the report from the skipper of a Grimsby trawler recently. For several days in the Shetlands area a succession of hurricanes had been experienced, ranging from 60 to 90 miles an hour, and in the midst of one of these storms a trawler, which was battling with the seas, received the following message from the Grimsby trawler *Veresis* which was homeward bound with a crew of 12 from Iceland : " Have been swept clean, losing bridge, both compasses and boats, crew all safe but not sound. Will any ship fitted with direction finding wireless take a bearing on us and come and give us a compass. Have been dodging about in hurricanes for thirty-six hours. Think we are somewhere off the Faroes." Seven trawlers responded to the call for help and the *Veresis* was able to set a course for Cape Wrath, helped on her way by other ships fitted with direction finders.

The Auto Alarm.

Safety of life and property at sea has always been regarded as the first and greatest advantage of wireless, but the smaller ships cannot afford to employ sufficient operators to keep a continuous wireless watch and there is the possibility that a distress call may be missed while the operator is off duty. This danger is now removed where the auto-alarm is installed. As has been mentioned in the previous chapter, had this device been invented and installed on ships carrying only one operator prior to the *Titanic* disaster it is certain that the loss of life then involved would have been greatly reduced. Most of the smaller vessels which carry only one operator are now equipped with this apparatus. When the operator goes off duty he turns a switch which connects the aerial to the auto alarm, thus setting the apparatus in readiness to ring alarm bells on receipt of a special signal known as the Alarm Signal. If a fault develops in the alarm apparatus itself the bell also rings and calls attention to the apparatus being out of order. One of the units of the apparatus is a sensitive selector which only permits the bell circuits to be completed upon the receipt of the special alarm signal. It is only possible to stop the bells ringing by changing over the switch in the wireless room, and so disconnecting the auto alarm and reverting to the main receiver. Thus the operator recalled in this way is able to resume his watch in time to receive the necessary information from the ship in distress. This means that with the general adoption of auto alarm apparatus even the smallest ship would receive intimation of the call for help in its neighbourhood and in consequence might materially reduce the time taken in coming to the assistance of the disabled vessel.

The Band Repeater and Music Player.

Apart from the more serious applications of wireless for marine purposes, there is the field of entertainment. A number of subsidiary devices have been developed as a result of the stimulus given to invention by the needs of broadcasting. Among these are the *band repeater* and *music player*. These instruments employ certain wireless principles in the form of microphone and amplifier circuits, and are particularly suitable for providing music in various parts of a ship. The band repeater is the largest installation, and is capable of repeating in large deck spaces the music of an orchestra played in some central part of a ship, or of repeating gramophone music by means of powerful sound reproducers. The music player is more suitable for smaller spaces, and amplifies and repeats the orchestra, or reproduces gramophone records by means of a special electric pick-up device. This instrument is a great boon on small ships which normally do not carry an orchestra but where music is at times desirable, as with it gramophone records can be reproduced with perfect clarity and at sufficient volume for dancing.

Marine Wireless Telephony.

Ship telephony was first made use of commercially by the fishing industry. Fishing vessels generally cannot afford to carry an operator, and wireless telephone sets were consequently designed, in such a form that the crew could learn how to manipulate the apparatus without any difficulty. Telephony was an essential for such a service, as it could not be expected that the fisherman should learn the Morse code. Trawlers and small vessels are not required by international regulations to carry wireless telegraphy, but the introduction of cheap and simple telephone sets for the use of fishing vessels soon demonstrated the utility of this service to the fishing industry, and now a large and increasing number of trawlers, whalers and fishing vessels are equipped. Around the coast of Great Britain and Ireland a complete chain of wireless telephone installations has been set up to meet the demands of the fishing industry. Messages transmitted by telephony from ships to these coast stations, are conveyed by telegram to their destination on land, while telegrams for the ships equipped with telephone sets are telephoned on from the coastal station. Ships fitted with these telephone equipments are able to speak to the shore from the fishing grounds, and to keep in touch with one another for the exchange of information in regard to weather and fishing conditions. They can speak to the port authorities and fix up details in regard to docking and landing, and ascertain from their headquarters the marketing conditions at the local ports ; information which may have a considerable effect on the financial results of the voyage. Furthermore, gale warnings broadcast to shipping have on many occasions been the means of saving nets and other fishing gear.

The utility of short wave working for long distance communication brought about the extensive use of wireless telephony on board ship for various purposes. One of the earliest applications made of this form of communication was the installation of short wave telephone sets on board the whalers operating in the extreme South Seas. The sets, designed for this class of vessel, were completely enclosed in metal cabinets, and provided with an external handle to control the generator and to change over from transmission to reception ; they therefore did not require the services of a telegraphist and could be operated by the ship personnel. At the base of the whaling industry on South Georgia the office of the Manager was similarly equipped, so that not only could the whalers talk to each other but with their base. The advent of short wave wireless led to its adoption on some of the whaling vessels, and by its means they were able to get into direct touch with the home ports in Norway.

While ship telephony has been in use for some time past for communication between trawlers, whalers and other types of fishing vessels, a new type of wireless telephone service has recently been developed on much more ambitious lines, whereby certain liners are connected through the radio link to the public telephone services of the various countries effecting this new form of marine service. This class of communication is essentially a luxury service. It is not likely to be installed except on the more important liners carrying a large number of first class passengers, since the apparatus involved is necessarily elaborate and its cost consequently high, entailing high charges for a few minutes conversation. While from the ship-owner's point of view the advertisement value of having a public ship to shore telephone service available may be substantial, the actual revenue received from the tolls is unlikely to cover the cost of operating the service, and the interest on the capital invested in the equipment.

The difficulties that have to be surmounted in effecting satisfactory public telephonic communication from and to a ship at sea are very considerable. The space available on board ship limits the size and type of transmitter ; directive aerials giving a large multiplying factor to the signal strength cannot be installed. The continuously changing distance over which the ship has to work necessitates the use of several wavelengths. Furthermore, the type of ship upon which a telephone service of this nature is required has also to maintain several other essential services, working on short and medium wavelengths, as well as the 600 and 800 metre service for normal ship communication. All these services, involving both transmission and reception, have to be effected simultaneously, and independently of the telephone service, without mutual interference, and the different aerials for these various services must necessarily be close together. The waves have to be most carefully selected to avoid a possible harmonic of the longer waves interfering with telephony. There is an added difficulty, namely the re-radiation from the rigging, etc., of the oscillations generated by the powerful radiation from the ship's own short wave transmitting aerials. This last difficulty has been minimised by the adoption of the principle of carrier suppression, that is to say, the suppression of the radiation from the transmitter during the moments of reception, but even so the problem of interference is a serious one and close cooperation between the telegraphist and telephone operator is essential.

The first ships equipped with this type of installation worked on the four-wire principle, that is to say, with separate pairs of leads to the telephone receiver and microphone, but the development of this type of service is extending. The more recently fitted ships have been equipped with the two-wire system as in land telephony, involving the necessity of providing telephone terminal equipment as at the shore end, and entailing thereby still greater expense in the ship installation. As has already been mentioned, the choice of wavelengths is one of considerable difficulty, but with suitable wavelengths it is now practicable for a ship fitted with this class of telephone installation to call up anyone or any telephone exchange from even the most distant seas.

CHAPTER XV

WIRELESS FOR AVIATION

THE position of the aeroplane in mid air is similar to that of the ship in mid ocean so far as communication with land bases is concerned. The main difference is that efficient communication at all times is in some respects even more important to the airman than the seaman. In case of fog or weather conditions unsuitable for making port, a ship not fitted with some form of wireless can go dead slow, or heave to if necessary, but when caught in a fog or storm the aeroplane has to proceed and find its way to a safe landing. Wireless is thus a necessity to aircraft if they are to maintain a regular flying schedule in the face of all contingencies, such as clouds, mists, storms and fog banks, and ever-changing weather conditions.

Experiments were carried out as early as 1912 in Air to Ground wireless at the Graham White establishment at Hendon, but, as has been indicated, the real impetus to intensive research came during the war, and by the time that commercial air services were inaugurated, after the signing of the Peace Treaty, it was possible to provide a system of wireless communication that was of material assistance in the conduct of the new aviation services. In this connection it is interesting to recall that when the de Havilland aeroplane made its first commercial flights between London and Paris in August 1919 it was fitted with Marconi apparatus.

As a result of the experience gained during and after the war it is now accepted that the practical utility of aviation, both military and civil, is greatly increased with the advances made in the organization and technical efficiency of aircraft and aerodrome wireless systems. Whether used as a fighting unit, as an " Air Liner," or simply as a convenient means of rapid travel, the aeroplane, flying boat or lighter-than-air craft, like the ship at sea, is not fully efficient unless able to

PLATE XII

CROYDON AERODROME CONTROL TOWER WITH MAST
SUPPORTING DIRECTION FINDING AERIAL

keep in touch with land bases. The rapid and continuous progress made in the reliability and range of modern aircraft has necessitated the development of an efficient system of wireless services for aviation purposes. The pivots of this organization are the Air Ports equipped with wireless to provide for the distribution of meteorological information, route traffic between air ports, communication between air ports and aircraft, and direction and position finding.

Meteorological Information

While the design of modern aircraft, and the services of wireless have today rendered flying possible under weather conditions that only a few years ago would have been regarded as prohibitive, the state of the weather is still an important factor in aviation. One of the first aids of wireless to aircraft is therefore the rapid circulation of information about weather conditions, which is particularly valuable on air routes in parts of the world where climatic conditions are liable to rapid change. In many cases the decision as to whether it is possible to proceed on a journey or whether to return to the nearest clear air port will depend solely on the information given to the pilot as to the weather ahead.

When it is appreciated that the safety of passengers and machine may depend on the rapid and accurate distribution of weather information it is evident that wireless communication for the meterological services must be highly efficient. The meteorological services are carried out in England, as is natural, by the Air Ministry, and the service rendered and organization schemed out and put into effect is in every way admirable.

Meteorological information is usually circulated between air ports in the form of long figure code messages, but when it is necessary to pass this information to the pilots in the air telephony is used or the telegram is sent " en clair."

Route Traffic between Air Ports.

Where an organized air route is established between fixed points it is essential that an efficient system of wireless communication should exist in order that messages may be communicated without delay concerning the departure and arrival of the aircraft, landing instructions, information regarding passengers and goods, and the many points which are essential to the smooth working of an efficient air organization. The exchange of similar information is equally of value between civil air ports dealing with independent or private aircraft, as a constant check on the number of machines in the air at any time can thus be kept.

The normal route traffic messages, consisting of information regarding times of departure, numbers of passengers, letters defining the aircraft, and so on, are transmitted in Morse code, a permanent record of the messages sent and received being kept. To prevent congestion of service a simple code is employed for these messages.

Communication with Aircraft.

For communication from the air ports to pilots in the air telephony is usually employed, but in the case of large passenger planes, the normal practice is for a wireless operator to be carried, and for long distance communication, telegraphy is employed.

The range over which it is possible for air ports and aircraft to keep in touch with one another naturally depends on the type, power, design and efficiency of the wireless equipment used, and also on the wavelength employed.

The types of wireless apparatus for use in military aircraft vary very largely. For one class of service long range communication is required, for communication between individual machines flying in military formation a different type of apparatus with very short range is necessary, while for artillery cooperation with aeroplanes yet another type is needed. In the field of commercial aviation medium wave transmitters and receivers are used for the approach to the aerodrome, and for general purposes in ordinary daily flights between fixed points on established services, but for very long flights, such as the route from Cairo to the Cape, it has been found essential to equip the aeroplanes with short wave apparatus in addition, since the atmospherics on this route are very severe and frequently drown all possibility of communication when medium waves are used. It is interesting to note that aeroplanes equipped with short wave apparatus, flying on the Cape route, have been able to keep in touch with European stations without difficulty. Wireless apparatus for aircraft has to conform to special requirements of lightness, compactness and robustness, combined with an ability to resist damage, due to vibration or the sudden shock of a bad landing.

The use of short wave apparatus on aircraft is likely to grow, involving new problems, while the increasing use of telephony further complicates design. For medium waves simple self-oscillators can be utilized, but with short waves this is not the case, as variations in the carrier frequency, caused by modulation, distort the received speech. This can only be overcome by the provision of a master oscillator having a high degree of constancy, and the problem of design is further complicated by the necessity of the transmitter being able to change over from one to another of several different wavelengths rapidly. Most of these various problems have been tackled by the specialists who devote their whole time to the design of modern aircraft apparatus, but doubtless, although a high degree of excellency in design and performance has already been attained, further improvements will be effected.

Many romantic stories could be told of the services which wireless on aeroplanes has rendered both in times of peace and war. It has assisted Atlantic flyers to success and has saved the lives of others whose machines have failed and have come down, sometimes in desolate and uninhabited regions. Over the forests of Canada it has given warning of incipient fires and directed the activities of fire fighters. It has helped in the chase and capture of criminals. It has responded to the calls for medical assistance, for flying ambulances from remote pioneers, in Canada, Australia, South America and other part of the world, who are weeks away from the nearest doctor by land or water, but only hours by air. Furthermore, during the American expedition to the South Polar area, constant communication was effected from an aeroplane between Admiral Byrd's expedition direct with the American mainland. During the war the aeroplanes cooperating with the artillery, directing their fire on hostile batteries or on other objects, were fitted with wireless transmitters and sent

L

down their observations to the ground stations. Day by day pilots would go up over the enemy's line, for a flight generally lasting three hours, continuously being fired at by anti-aircraft guns, frequently attacked by hostile planes, but flying backwards and forwards between the target and the battery, occasionally twisting and turning in one direction or the other to avoid the bursts of the shells, but always sending down the position of each shell as it fell near its object until the gun was accurately registered and a direct hit on the target recorded. Sometimes the aeroplane saw movement of hostile troops in mass formation or roads full of hostile transport, in which case the actual position in the map square would be sent and an emergency call for artillery concentration on the new target would quickly disperse or destroy the enemy concentration. I well remember one particular incident when watching a shoot at one of our batteries directed by an aeroplane on a hostile battery. Our guns had registered a hit on one enemy gun and switched over to the next when the pilot sent us a message to wait a moment as he was being attacked by hostile aircraft. We were very anxious for his safety as he was flying an old type of slow machine and at that particular period of the war the enemy machines were much faster; several minutes passed by in silence and anxiety when suddenly to our relief he sent us the signal to continue the shoot, and it was only later, on his return to the aerodrome, that we learned that he had shot one plane down and driven off the other. The romantic episodes in which wireless figured during the war are beyond enumeration, but I mention this incident from my personal experience.

Direction and Position Finding.

One of the most valuable uses of wireless for aircraft is the opportunity it affords of ascertaining the position at any time of aircraft in flight.

While the ordinary methods of navigation can be used with reasonable success in the air, in certain weather conditions these methods may become misleading and in some cases impossible. Pilots, surrounded by thick fog, cannot navigate by visual observation and reference has to be made to the compass and dead reckoning. The difficulty of correcting for compass errors and for wind drift make it practically impossible for the pilot to determine his exact position by these means, and if the fog belt extended for many miles it is possible he may become lost unless the aid of wireless direction finding services can be summoned. Practically all modern aeroplanes are therefore equipped with direction finding apparatus as well as with the ordinary gear for communication purposes. A pilot in doubt as to his position can call up an air port and ask for his exact bearings to be given him. This is done by two or three ground stations working in cooperation. From their joint observations the position of the aeroplane at the moment is worked out and the information transmitted to the pilot. With practised operators, when a position is asked for, the information can be given in less than one minute and a half. So precise has this method of navigation become that on many occasions pilots have flown between Croydon and the Continent, when the ground has been invisible practically throughout the flight, solely by this wireless guidance. Where such ground services are not available, or when other conditions make it desirable, aircraft may be fitted with their own wireless direction finding apparatus; but as it is usually essential on civil aircraft to reduce the number of the crew and the weight of the equipment to a minimum, the system of position finding from ground stations, which requires the carriage of no special apparatus, or increase in the number of the crew carried, is therefore generally relied upon.

On pioneer flights over ocean or undeveloped country the direction finder installed on the aircraft is of particular value, as it enables bearings to be taken of any type of wireless transmitting station, and in time of war would allow the airman to take his bearings without the risk of disclosing his position to the enemy. Most of the land direction finding stations have up to the present time been equipped with apparatus of the Bellini-Tosi type, but recently a very notable advance has been made by the development of the Adcock principle. This enables night errors in the recorded bearings to be eliminated. Important investigations in this field have been due to work carried out by the Radio Research

Board in England, while similar investigations have also been carried out by the Marconi Company on the directional characteristics of incoming radiation on short wavelengths. After further investigation on the short wave Adcock direction finder the Marconi Company adapted the technique developed, to the reception of medium waves. Certain modifications had to be made and prolonged tests with the new instrument showed the possibility, on wavelengths of the order of 1000 metres, of obtaining an accuracy in night reception of 2° to 3°. This result is of the utmost importance when it is realized that hitherto it has not been possible, with practicable commercial instruments, to ensure a definite degree of accuracy with continuous waves during the night period. It will readily be seen that this development will have an important bearing on aircraft navigation.

Comparative tests made with aircraft after sunset during "night effect" conditions over a distance of more than 50 miles showed that the limit of error with the Adcock arrangement did not exceed ±3°, whereas with the Bellini-Tosi method only a small proportion of observations gave an accuracy within ±3° and errors were recorded up to 90°. The very convincing results obtained with the Adcock direction finder, whereby freedom from night errors can be guaranteed on medium waves, points to the employment of this system in future coast and aerodrome stations and its gradual introduction in places where the Bellini-Tosi system is at present utilized.

Equi-Signal Beacons.

Another form of radio beacon has recently been developed in America to meet the case where the pilot does not require to know his exact position, but does want to know if he is flying on a true bearing to his destination. The underlying principle of the American radio beacon may be briefly described as follows : two directive aerials are placed at an angle with each other ; along the line bisecting this angle the radiation from each aerial is equal, at any other point radiation is stronger from one than the other. If therefore the radiation from each aerial can be clearly differentiated it becomes possible by observing the combined radiation to

keep to the course along the bisector referred to. In one
form of beacon on this principle the radiation from the two
aerials is distinguished by the letters N and A respectively,
the A signal being sent in the spaces of the N signal. If the
radiation from both aerials is being received on the plane
with equal strength the combination of the two letters gives
a continuous dash. Displacement to the right or left of the
correct direction of flight results in either the letter N or A
being received more strongly and the pilot is able to fly back
into his correct course. A modification of this type of beacon
has been developed by the Bureau of Standards of America,
in which the separate directional radiations are designated
by different modulated frequencies. For reception of this
type of signal on the aeroplane a visual indicator has been
developed. The output circuit of the receiver is fed to two
reed indicators, the first of which is resonant to one frequency
of modulation and the second to the other. If therefore the
plane is flying correctly on the line where the radiation from
the two aerials is equal both reeds vibrate equally, whereas
if the plane be off the line one or other of the reeds vibrates
more deeply and the other less deeply. A number of these
equi-signal beacons have been erected in America and in
Canada, while in England the Air Ministry is investigating
the suitability of this form of directional equipment for fixed
air routes and has had one installed at the Croydon Aerodrome
by the Marconi Company.

Aircraft Picture Transmission.

The development of facsimile and picture transmission for
commercial services between fixed stations led to the study
of the practicability of designing apparatus which could
be installed in an aeroplane, and so send down information
of what the observer sees to the ground station. It was
thought that this application might be of considerable
military value in enabling the aeroplane observer or pilot
to mark on a map square the actual objects of interest he
is flying over or send down a written message which would
be reproduced in facsimile at the ground station. An
apparatus has been developed which fulfils the necessary
requirements and has the following special features :

1. Independent synchronization at the transmitter and receiver.
2. No photo electric pick up system at the transmitter.
3. Messages to be transmitted are written in conducting ink or very soft pencil.
4. Messages at the transmitter and receiver remain stationary.

Actual flying experience has shown that it is possible to convey military intelligence between an aircraft and its base by this means up to distances of 150 miles. The aircraft was using a 160 watt transmitter on the normal aircraft wave, and the speed of transmission is approximately 9 square inches per minute.

Aerodrome Ground Stations.

The equipment of modern aerodromes with wireless apparatus to meet all the varying needs of wireless communication to and from other aerodromes and aeroplanes presents special problems.

The equipment must make provision for the rapid change by remote control to the transmitters of any one of four to six wavelengths in the band between 400 and 1600 metres. In important aerodromes several transmitters are provided to meet this requirement, while on those of minor importance, where expense has to be taken seriously into consideration, the transmitter has to be designed with several wavelengths to meet this special need. The increasing tendency to equip aeroplanes with short wave apparatus for long distance flights necessitates the provision of short wave transmitters and receivers at the aerodrome station also. Furthermore, the equipment must comprise complete installations for the guiding of the aeroplanes by means of direction finding beacons or direction finding receivers embodying the most modern methods. It will be perhaps of interest to describe the Croydon Aerodrome station, which is probably the best example of modern wireless organization and control for aviation services.

This aerodrome is the terminus of all commercial air lines flying to England. It was first equipped with wireless in 1920, but in 1928, after eight years of practical experience, a new and greatly improved system of wireless communication was devised and the requisite plant supplied by the Marconi Company for the Air Ministry. Four transmitters each of 4 K.W. input, working on different wavelengths, and direction finding receivers embodying the latest improvements in wireless technique, were installed for communication with other aerodromes and with aircraft in flight. The wireless control of aeroplanes and the direction finding services are centred in the Aerodrome Control Tower. In the wireless room in this tower a wireless officer is in constant touch with the aeroplanes in flight. He is in control of the direction finding receiver and of three of the four transmitters at the transmitting station at Mitcham, erected some $2\frac{1}{2}$ miles from the aerodrome. One of these transmitters is arranged to transmit telephony on 930 metres wavelength, the second telegraphy on 870 metres, and the third is a standby for emergency use on 900 metres. The fourth transmitter is controlled from the separate Route Traffic wireless room. All these transmitters can, however, work on any wavelength between 800 and 2000 metres, a change of wavelength being merely a matter of adjustment.

Some distance from the Control Tower is the Route Traffic room, where communication is maintained on the wavelength of 1300 metres with other aerodromes, for the exchange of messages dealing with the departure of aircraft and other service matters. The wireless officer in the Control Tower and in the Route Traffic Office work independently of each other. All messages received, either from aircraft or from other aerodromes are, however, passed to the Aerodrome Officer on duty in the Control Tower. Direction finding stations at other aerodromes at Lympne and Pulham collaborate with the Croydon aerodrome. When a pilot of a plane sends a request to Croydon for his position, Pulham and Lympne, at which stations a constant watch is kept, simultaneously take his bearings. These bearings are at once passed on to Croydon by wireless, and these together with Croydon bearings are plotted on a large map and where they cross is the position of the aeroplane. This reading is then sent to the aeroplane by Croydon.

Since the plant mentioned above has been installed the Air Ministry have added to the Aerodrome wireless equipment the installation of a visual beam transmitter. This consists of two loop aerials fixed at right angles to one another as in the Bellini-Tosi system. These aerials are each excited from a continuous wave transmitter. The high frequency oscillations induced in each loop are modulated at different frequencies, one at 65 periods a second, the other at 86·7 periods a second. The visual signal receiver, which is installed in the aircraft, consists of a receiver operating a small visual indicator comprising two reeds, one resonant to the frequency of 65 periods a second, the other to the frequency of 86·7. If the receiver is tuned to the carrier wave and the aircraft flown towards the beacons, the reeds will vibrate and the amplitude of the vibration of each reed will depend upon the strength of the low frequency modulations received from the relatively modulated field.

If the aircraft deviates to either side of the correct course then the signal due to one aerial will be of greater intensity than the other and therefore the amplitude of the vibration of the two reeds will be unequal, hence all the pilot has to do is to swing to the right or to the left until the vibrations are equal and he is on his correct course. The reed indicator provides an optical method of direction, thereby relieving the pilot of the strain of concentrating for long periods on aurally received signals. Another advantage has been found, namely, that the natural selectivity of the reeds effectively reduces interference caused by other transmitting stations and by the ignition system of the aircraft engines.

PLATE XIII

RADIO TELEPHONE TERMINAL CONTROL AT POST OFFICE, LONDON

[face p. 169

CHAPTER XVI

BRITISH POST OFFICE CONTRIBUTION TO WIRELESS
DEVELOPMENT

THE great State organization, known as the Post Office,
which holds the monopoly for inland telegraphy and
telephony in Great Britain, has played a considerable part
in the development of wireless, particularly in the direction
of wireless " Telephony ".

The possibility of communicating over space without the
use of connecting wires attracted the attention of Post Office
engineers as early as 1886. The most promising method at
that time was the earth conduction system, whereby currents
in a line, earthed at each end, induced currents in another
line parallel to it and similarly earthed but displaced laterally
from it. Distances up to 40 miles were worked by this
method and two or three telegraph circuits were operated on
this principle.

Mention has already been made of the assistance given to
Marconi by Sir William Preece, then Engineer-in-Chief of
the Post Office, when the former first arrived in England, and
this assistance continued until the Wireless Company was
formed.

The obvious field for wireless exploitation was in establishing communication with ships at sea, and the monopoly of
the Post Office did not cover this service. The Government,
however, saw the danger of the indiscriminate use of wireless
for this purpose, and wisely decided that no one should
operate a wireless station without a licence, and constituted
the Postmaster-General the licensing authority. The Post
Office was therefore officially concerned with the development
of wireless from its first practical application. At the beginning of the twentieth century there was no other wireless
organization in the field, and the Marconi Company gradually
extended its marine services, and built a series of wireless
stations around the coasts of Great Britain and Ireland, for

communication with the rapidly increasing number of ships equipped with wireless. In 1904 the Post Office undertook the collection, transmission, and delivery of ship to shore, and long distance messages on behalf of the Marconi Company. In 1906 the Post Office gave a contract to the Marconi Company for the provision of two stations at Tobermory and Loch Boisdale in Scotland. In 1909 arrangements were made whereby the operation of the British coastal wireless stations was transferred from the control of the Marconi Company to the Post Office, and from that date the Post Office has owned and operated all the British stations for working with ships at sea. Meanwhile other rival systems to the Marconi system had come into the field, such as the Poulsen, De Forest, and Fessenden systems. All these were carefully investigated and tried out by the Post Office engineers. Between 1909 and 1913 the Post Office reorganized the coastal wireless stations, re-equipping some, and building others in more suitable localities, and gradually built up a well organized shore to ship service, which has remained in operation to the present date.

The development of commercial wireless services was stopped by the Great War and the construction of the stations for the Post Office by the Marconi Company for Imperial communications was postponed. The energies of the Post Office were directed to assisting the fighting services with plant and material and, among other work, a number of direction finding stations were built, and manned by Post Office staff. These were for the detection and location of enemy aircraft and ships.

Mention has been made in a previous chapter of the fact that early in the war the Post Office cancelled the contract with the Marconi Company for the construction of the Imperial stations, and that the Courts awarded the Marconi Company damages amounting to nearly six hundred thousand pounds. Although this award was substantial, and of immediate benefit to the shareholders, it had in reality a most unfortunate result for the Marconi Company. The award of these heavy damages against the Post Office made its officials very reluctant to enter into new contracts with the Company. At this date, however, there was no other British organization possessing the knowledge and experience of long distance commercial wireless, and the Post Office felt itself therefore in a difficult position in that there was no other Company with which it could negotiate ; this led to the policy of building up a large wireless organization in the Post Office itself and to the training and development of what has become a highly efficient technical staff. As a result, much work which would otherwise have been placed out to contract has been carried out by the engineers of the Post Office themselves.

Very early in the war the Post Office contracted with the Marconi Company for the erection of an emergency wireless station in Egypt, to serve strategic purposes for direct communication with England. At the termination of the war the Government agreed to the Post Office proposal to organize a commercial radio-telegraphic service between England and Egypt. After considering the different systems, available at that date, the Post Office decided to instal the Poulsen system. The extension and alterations of the Egyptian station and the Post Office station at Leafield in England were completed in 1921 and a wireless service was worked for several years until the Egyptian station was finally sold to the Marconi Company. Meanwhile the Post Office had effected an outstanding improvement in the Poulsen arcs by enabling them to be operated in conjunction with coupled circuits, resulting in a gain in purity of the emitted waves, and an improved frequency constancy.

In 1923 the Post Office introduced the first cooled anode valves to be used in England. These, designed and manufactured by the Western Electric Company of America, were fitted to a valve transmitter which the Post Office had constructed at their medium power station at Northolt.

The progress in development of receivers, and the increasing congestion of the frequency spectrum, made it imperative that the frequency of transmitting stations be maintained as near constant as possible. The Post Office engineers turned their attention to this problem and in collaboration with Dr. Eccles, their Consulting Engineer, developed the " tuning fork " method of control. An experimental equipment was built in which a tuning fork vibrating between 1000 and 2000 times a second was used as a source of constant frequency, and a suitable harmonic of this frequency was selected, amplified and used to control the frequency of the Northolt transmitter. The results were so successful that the installation was made permanent, and a similar control applied to all high power valve transmitters subsequently constructed by the Post Office. The invention of the tuning fork method of control, due to Dr. Eccles and the Post Office engineers, was an important contribution to technical development, and this method of control remains today one of the three methods whereby constancy of control can be achieved.

In 1923 the Government decided to erect a high-power long wave station in England for Imperial and world communications, and that this station should be built by the Post Office. A site 1½ square miles in extent was selected near Rugby and the station, equipped with twelve 820 feet masts and a 500 kw. transmitter using water-cooled valves, was completed in 1925. A brief description of this station is given in an earlier chapter. The invention of the short wave beam provided a much more rapid, effective, and cheap method of communication between fixed points than could be achieved by any long wave transmitting station however powerful. The original purpose of the Rugby station was therefore otherwise effected. There were, however, other useful services which could be provided by the Rugby station, particularly a long distance service to ships at sea. The importance to a country such as Great Britain of being able to communicate immediately and simultaneously to British ships on all seas needs no emphasis. News bulletins are broadcast daily to all parts of the Empire and to British ships on the high seas. Radio telegrams are transmitted to ships in any part of the world. Time signals are also transmitted twice a day direct from the Greenwich Observatory for astronomical and navigational purposes, with an accuracy of the order of 1/100th of a second.

Although the Rugby high-power long wave telegraph transmitter designed and constructed by the Post Office engineers was and is still the most powerful yet constructed, the Rugby wireless station is chiefly notable as the European centre of wireless telephone communication, and the great contribution to the technical development of wireless, made by the Post Office engineers, is exemplified in the equipment of the wireless telephone apparatus installed at Rugby, and at the Post Office corresponding receiving stations, and in the special terminal apparatus installed at the Central Control Office in London.

The subject of wireless telephony had been an attractive one to inventors for many years prior to the invention of the thermionic valve, but an insuperable obstacle to development of large power transmitters was the difficulty of modulating such oscillators as were available. The advent of the high powered valve made long distance radio telephony a practical possibility. Prior to the war knowledge was vague as to the width of the frequency band necessary for any particular type of radio communication. It was realized that the modulation of the carrier frequency either wholly by a telegraph key, or partially by telephony, produced interference on adjoining frequencies, and that the higher the speed of signalling, the greater the width of interference, but the extent of this interference had not been determined quantitatively.

One of the most important and far-reaching inventions, made in 1913, was the discovery by an engineer of the Post Office, Mr. G. M. B. Shepperd, of the wave filter. In its basic conception the filter was of two types, one the high pass type which blocked the passage of currents of all frequencies below a certain value, known as the cut-off frequency, but gave unhindered passage to currents of frequencies above this value. The second type, known as the low pass type, had converse properties, and gave unhindered passage to currents of frequencies below the cut-off frequency, but obstructed all frequencies above this value. By means of these filters it became possible to investigate the bands of frequencies actually necessary for the conveyance of speech and music, and to ascertain the effects on intelligibility of speech of the elimination of frequencies above and below certain fixed values. This discovery opened the way, not only to an improvement in the selectivity of receivers, but also to the development of carrier current telephony, whereby a number of telephone conversations could be carried on simultaneously on a single pair of wires.

The properties of wave filters were investigated mathematically by Carson and Zobel of the Bell Telephone Laboratories in America, who are responsible for the invention of a number of improved types.

The currents used for commercial telephony occupy a band in the spectrum of from about 300 to 3000 cycles : for the transmission of good quality music the band occupied ranges from about 30 to 10,000 cycles. Telegraphy, on the other hand, with its much lower frequency of modulation requires a total band of from 60 to 600 cycles for the transmission of signals from 25 to 250 words per minute.

The problem of transmitting speech by wireless from one point and receiving this speech at a distant point was largely a matter of power at the transmitter, and sensitivity and selectivity at the receiver, and came within the domain of the radio engineer, but if radio telephony were to be generally useful it had to be possible to extend the radio circuit at each terminal on to the telephone network of the country in which it was situated. This requirement opened up a fresh and formidable series of problems, the solution of which required the specialized knowledge of telephone engineers as well as radio engineers working in close cooperation.

During the years in which radio technique had been developing similar progress had been made in line telephony. Research had disclosed the characteristics of human speech, and the frequency bands necessary for its effective and intelligible propagation. The problem of introducing inductance in the form of loading on long distance telephone lines in order to preserve the higher frequency of speech had been solved, and finally the application of the valve in repeaters on long circuits had been successfully effected. The latter development made practicable the use of light gauge conductors in underground cables in place of heavy overhead wires and thus opened the way to a wide extension of telephone trunk facilities. Normal telephone practice requires that both the outgoing and incoming speech currents for a subscriber shall be effected over a single pair of wires. The application of an amplifier to such a circuit presents difficulties in as much as the amplifier must operate in both directions, and an obvious solution has been the provision of two amplifiers, one to operate in one direction, while the other operates in the reverse direction. This practice introduces a fresh difficulty in that the output of each amplifier is connected to the input circuit of the other, with the result that any initial disturbance of signal, no matter how insignificant, is amplified repeatedly, and the whole equipment breaks into oscillation, a condition known technically as " singing." The solution has been found in an electrical balancing arrangement, whereby the output from one amplifier is prevented from feeding the input of the other ; this demands the provision of a circuit having electrical characteristics identical with those of the line itself. No balance of this kind can, however, be perfect, and in practice the greater the amount by which the balance falls short of perfection the less the amount of amplification which can be obtained in a repeater. In practice, however, where a high grade of maintenance of equipment is observed and other necessary precautions taken, stable operation of long "repeatered" lines is attained. Even in these circumstances trouble is liable to occur on a long line, due to a portion of the speech currents from the distant talker being reflected at the receiving point, and passed back along the circuit through the other set of amplifiers, thus producing the sensation of echo in the ear of the speaker. This defect has been overcome by a device which renders one or more of the amplifiers in one direction inoperative while speech is passing in the other direction. Devices for this purpose are known as " Echo Suppressors," and notable improvements in such apparatus have been introduced by Post Office engineers by the application of thermionic valves to their operation.

It has been the aim of the Post Office engineers to provide throughout the British Isles a network of trunk circuits of the highest possible quality, so that the inclusion of such a circuit between two subscribers in distant parts of the country incurs no deterioration or loss in speech currents. As a result a subscriber in London can at the present time speak to a subscriber, say, in Edinburgh with as little effort as he can speak to another subscriber in London, and the complete ideal is within sight of realization, and with it the additional facility of obtaining connection between distant parts of the country on demand without any period of waiting, and with the same expedition with which a local connection is obtained. The degree of perfection in long line telephony that has been attained has only been achieved by precise knowledge of the properties of line circuits and their associated equipment, for which accurate methods of measurement had to be devised. The utilization of radio circuits for telephony demanded the application of equally accurate measurements to radio equipment, and circuits, and the association of radio with telephony has been of inestimable benefit to the development of radio technique in demanding a precision of performance of equipment which had hitherto been unattained.

The telephone engineer looks upon the radio transmitter and receiver as two large amplifiers in the telephone circuit, and is not satisfied unless he can be assured that these links will function in a similar manner. Provided that a radio circuit has perfectly constant characteristics it can be included in a telephone circuit in the same way as a four-wire trunk circuit, but only on short wireless circuits does this condition hold good. In the case of long distance circuits, subject to great variations in strength and quality, it becomes necessary not only to interrupt completely, and to hold interrupted, the circuit in one direction while speech is passing in the other direction, and vice versa, but also to interrupt the transmitting link on each side during the periods when speech is not being passed. Such switching operations must, however, be performed automatically by the speech currents themselves, and yet the equipment must not be operated by sporadic noises introduced into the circuits from other sources. In long radio circuits of this kind the radio transmitter and radio receiver are in reality two gigantic repeaters whose power amplification is of the order of above one thousand million.

It has been previously stated that the British Government authorized the Post Office to construct an extra high-power wireless station for Imperial and World communications in 1923. The work was at once put in hand. At this date the

Post Office decided to cooperate with the American Telephone and Telegraph Company in an attempt to provide a transatlantic telephone service. This was a very bold decision, as nothing of a similar kind had hitherto been contemplated or attempted, and very little was known of the requirements of such a circuit beyond the fact that it would have to be many times superior to any existing transatlantic telegraph service, and yet the cost of operation would have to be kept to a minimum if the circuit were to be a commercial success. The authorization by the Government for the provision of a transmitter of much greater power than any yet erected gave a possibility that the transmitted energy from such a transmitter might render radio telephony across the Atlantic practicable.

In radio telegraphy the full power of the transmitter is utilized for every signal transmitted, while the energy is concentrated in a narrow band of frequencies usually not exceeding 200 to 300 cycles in width. In radio telephony, on the other hand, the full power of the transmitter must be available, but is rarely used as, owing to the inflections of normal speech, the greater portions of the speech (which must be transmitted perfectly if intelligibility is to be assured) may contain less than one thousandth of the louder or accented portions which call for the full power of the transmitter. In telephony moreover, the energy radiated is spread over a much wider band of frequencies, the minimum width of which cannot be less than 3000 cycles per second, that is to say more than ten times the width of a telegraph channel. The transmission of the wider band demands a proportionately better circuit than is necessary for the narrower band. Thus the whole problem called for an extensive amount of research covering the fields of transmission, of reception, and of terminal apparatus.

An exhaustive investigation on reception was undertaken and lasted for several years, to determine the optimum wavelength for transatlantic service, the transmission conditions throughout the twenty-four hours, and throughout the year, the best location for the receiving station, and the most suitable type of receiving equipment. This investigation disclosed that the best wavelength was of the order of 5000

M

metres, and that the most favourable location for the receiving
station would be as far north as possible, also that some form
of directive receiving aerial would be required.

In the transmission problem the development of line
telephony by the engineers of the American Telephone and
Telegraph Company offered a means of increasing the effective
power of the transmitter about six times by the adoption of
the single side band suppressed carrier system. The adoption
of this system had the additional advantage that the band
of frequencies necessary would be limited to 3000 cycles
instead of 6000 cycles, a very important consideration in view
of the congestion in the ether on the longer wavelengths. It
was decided therefore to adopt the single side band system
and also, owing to wavelength congestion, that it would be
necessary to utilize the same frequency band for transmission
in both directions.

The adoption of a single frequency channel called for more
stringent requirements in the design of the terminal equipment, which now had to protect the receiving circuit from
the enormous signal picked up by the receiver from the local
transmitter, and yet respond to the comparatively weak
signals received from the distant transmitter.

The Post Office, in cooperation with the Western Electric
Company, installed at the Rugby station a telephone transmitter capable of delivering 200 kilowatts of power to an
aerial supported by four of the 820-feet masts. A receiving
site was selected at Cupar in Scotland and on this site a
directive aerial system was erected covering an area of several
square miles.

Radio telephony is particularly vulnerable to atmospherics,
owing to the wide band of frequencies which have to be
received, and as there was a very definite economic limit to
the signal which could be employed at the transmitting
station, most of the improvement in the radio circuit had of
necessity to be obtained in the receiver equipment. The
form of aerial used at the receiving station was therefore
very important, and the final design evolved by the Post
Office consisted of eight separate antenna units, spread over
an area of several square miles, each circuit comprising a
pair of antennae of different types, which, when combined,

had inherent direction properties. The signals from these antenna units were conveyed by overhead transmission lines to the receiving station, where the whole of the signals were combined in such a way as to give a highly directive reception in the direction of America.

The receivers used are provided with high and low pass filters which exclude all frequencies except those lying within the required band, and incorporate many novel features, such as the provision of measuring equipment, in order that the various circuits can be maintained continuously in the highest state of efficiency.

The terminal equipment in London was located in the trunk exchange building, and included amplifiers in the receiving and transmitting circuits, so that the levels of the incoming and outgoing speech currents could be adjusted to the correct values. There, also, was located the voice-operated device, which controls the passage of currents in the transmitting and receiving links according to the course of conversation. The device also prevents reception by the speaker of the signals from the local transmitting station, and restrains any tendency for the circuit as a whole to break into oscillation. Two types of this device, known as " Singing Suppressors " are in use—one devised by the engineers of the American Telephone and Telegraph Company, and the other by the Post Office engineers. The former utilizes electro-mechanical switches for making automatically the necessary connections and disconnections, whereas the latter utilizes thermionic valves, and is a development of the thermionic valve echo suppressor previously alluded to. Before the telephone channel could be regarded as completed it was necessary to apply correcting devices at each end so that the overall frequency characteristic of the circuit was substantially uniform.

This long wave transatlantic telephone circuit was opened for commercial traffic on 7th January 1927 for calls between London and New York. Since that date the service has gradually been extended to include the whole of North America, Mexico, and Cuba on the one side, and the whole of Europe, with a few minor exceptions, on the other. These extensions have been made possible by the great improvements that have taken place in landline trunk telephone systems on the lines previously indicated in this chapter. The service is at the present day still further extended by connection to other radio telephone channels which have since come into being. The reliability of the circuit approaches that of a trunk line and is available to traffic for well over 90 per cent of the time throughout the year.

By the time the long wave telephone service with America had been inaugurated, the Marconi Company had constructed under contract with the Post Office the short wave beam stations for telegraphic communication with the Dominions, and these were completely successful. Their success at once indicated to the Post Office the practicability of utilizing short waves for telephone communication, not only to supplement the existing American service but also for services with Australia, South Africa, and elsewhere.

The success of the beam services had threatened the Cable Companies with annihilation, and owing to the strategic importance of the Cable system, the Government withdrew the beam stations from the Post Office, and handed them over to a new Company to operate jointly with the Cables and thus avoid disastrous competition. The Government however reserved to the Post Office the duty of providing the overseas radio telephone services from England.

The Post Office engineers proceeded to develop actively short wave equipments for telephone purposes. It was soon realized that for successful telephony a high degree of constancy of frequency was necessary, as the slightest tendency for the frequency of the transmitter to fluctuate with modulation was productive of severe distortion in the received signals. For this reason the Post Office engineers made use of quartz crystal drives to ensure constancy. The importance of directing the transmitted wave was of course realized, but the Post Office engineers were unwilling to commit themselves rigidly to the form of beam aerial invented by the Marconi Company. Subsequent to the success of the Beam services the American, French, German, and Dutch had devised beam aerials differing in detail from the Franklin design, and these were tried out by the Post Office. Another factor influenced the Post Office decision as to the type of aerial to be used, namely, that the utility of any given wavelength could not be relied upon to remain constant throughout the year, or from year to year, and that consequently a considerable number of wavelengths would be required. It was therefore deemed advisable to erect a multiplicity of low and comparatively cheap aerials rather than a smaller number of high and expensive ones. The same policy was also adopted for both transmitting and receiving aerials. A group of short wave transmitters with their directive aerials was therefore constructed at Rugby, and as the reception of short wave signals did not require a northern site a receiving site for short waves was chosen at Baldock in Hertfordshire.

The receivers used in the first instance were of Post Office design ; they were of the superheterodyne type and incorporated wave filters in the intermediate stage. One important feature was the provision of an automatic gain control device to counteract the effect of fading in the received signals. This is effected by utilizing part of the signal itself to reduce the gain of the intermediate amplifier in the receiver. Thus a strong signal reduced the gain or amplification, whereas a weak signal allows the amplifier to function with full gain. The device is very effective and by its use it is possible to obtain a signal output with scarcely noticeable variation in strength. The original equipment has been increased from time to time and now includes receivers manufactured by the Marconi Company, and the Standard Telephone Company, in addition to those manufactured by the Post Office.

The first short wave transatlantic service was opened in June 1928 in cooperation with the American Telephone and Telegraph Company, and two additional short wave channels were opened for this service during 1929. The channels were equipped with three, and in one case with four, wavelengths, so that a change of wavelength could be made in a very few minutes.

Following on the opening of short wave services to America, a telephone service from London to certain large transatlantic liners was opened early in 1930 and about the same time a telephone service was inaugurated between London and Australia. Additional services were provided between

London and Buenos Aires, London and Capetown and London and Cairo in 1932. A direct service to Canada was also opened that year, while constructional work is in progress for a direct service between London and India, which will also shortly be opened.

The short wave channels are cheaper to operate than the long wave channel, since the total cost of the plant is much less, the power utilized is less and the associated land lines shorter. For the transatlantic service the long wave has greater stability, as it is not affected by magnetic storms, but for very long distances the short wave provides the only practicable method of communication.

With the growth of traffic on the transatlantic service a second long wave channel has become necessary and the Post Office engineers have made preparations to provide that channel.

The transmission qualities of the short wave channels are sufficiently good to allow them to be interconnected, with the result that service can now be given between distant parts of the world through London—for example, commercial conversations take place between New Zealand and South America utilizing three radio channels: New Zealand to Australia, Australia—England and England—South America, a total route of about 17,000 miles. In the same way all services between North America and Egypt, South Africa and Australia are handled through London. As a result of these connections the London Radio Terminal can truthfully be described as the World's Trunk Exchange.

Before leaving the subject of commercial wireless telephony it is necessary to refer to one of the objections to its employment : this is the possibility of conversations being overheard by unauthorized persons. This objection was realized as a serious one both in America and in Europe and much has been done to remove the disability by the adoption, as far as possible, of privacy equipment on these services. The method, which was first made feasible in America, is to distort the subscriber's speech at the transmitting end in such a way that reception by an unauthorized listener is extremely difficult. After reception at the distant end the speech is restored to its original quality before passing on to the listener ; a similar process is also applied to speech in the reverse direction.

The great utility of short waves for long distance communication invited the investigation of the properties of still shorter waves, below 10 metres in length. Marconi has done some remarkable development in this field, and has successfully es ablished telephonic communication between certain points in Italy using wavelengths of the order of only 50 centimetres. The Standard Telephone Company have also studied the properties of ultra short wave communication and have given a successful demonstration of ultra short wave working across the Channel. The Post Office engineers have been working independently on the same lines, and on the development of apparatus in order to utilize these waves effectively. The outcome of this work as a result has been the recent establishment of an ultra short wave telephone link between Lavernock, on the South Wales coast, and Weston-Super-Mare, which is now in commercial use. This radio link is 12 miles long and supplants a land line circuit through Bristol of about 60 miles in length. The properties of these ultra short waves are, in many respects, more akin to light waves than those of radio waves and their range approximates very closely to that of a beam of light. This restricted range makes them particularly suited to short distance communication, such as across sea channels or tidal estuaries. Much is however yet to be learnt about their properties and, particularly in the case of the shorter waves measurable by centimetres rather than metres, how to design means of transmitting them with considerable power, and to design valves for such extremely short waves with a reasonably commercial length of life.

This chapter is an endeavour to describe the contributions to radio development by the Post Office engineers. To sum up their achievements, they have been responsible for the design and construction of the largest long wave transmitting station in the world. They have adapted the valve amplifier for telephone trunk circuits ; the invention of the high and low pass filters was a Post Office invention ; they have developed the telephone terminal units to a high degree of perfection, and have introduced in this country methods of circuit measurement in wireless commercial receivers. Many devices and improvements in radio telephone receivers are due to their initiative and by reason of the exacting requirements of telephonic reception their practice has influenced the design of general commercial telegraph receivers. Finally, they have built up a remarkable central radio trunk system and made arrangements with European countries whereby all Europe can be connected by radio through London to the most distant parts of the world, with the result that England has become the world's great centre of Radio-Telephonic communication.

PLATE XIV

ELECTRA HOUSE, VICTORIA EMBANKMENT

The new headquarters of Imperial and International Communications, in London. The head offices of Marconi's Wireless Telegraph Co., Ltd., and the Marconi International Marine Communication Co., Ltd., are also contained in this new building

[face p. 175

CHAPTER XVII

COMMERCIAL WIRELESS TELEGRAPH DEVELOPMENT

TO appreciate in which direction commercial needs demand further extensions of existing facilities, or different methods to those in use, in fine, to visualize in what manner present practice falls short of ideal performance, we must take stock of the existing conditions in each branch of applied wireless.

Commercial Point to Point Wireless Telegraph Communication.

There are many problems as yet unsolved in the important field of wireless point to point telegraph communication. Although the invention of short wave beam wireless has profoundly altered the technique, and increased the capabilities of wireless commercial services, there are still a number of formidable difficulties to be overcome before short wave long distance wireless can be relied upon to ensure a constant high speed regular and continuous means of telegraphic communication. Before the invention of the short wave beam system wireless telegraph communication over long distances was carried out by long waves. The speed of signalling was slow, reception was greatly interfered with by atmospherics, and the range of long wave stations was limited to about 3000 miles for an effective telegraph service. Furthermore, such long wave stations were very costly and the number of stations that could be erected without mutual interference on the long waves necessary for reliable communication was strictly limited.

Long wave services, however, do not suffer from sudden or prolonged interruptions, as in the case of short waves, due to magnetic storms, of the effects of momentary changes in the condition of the Heaviside layer, from which short waves are reflected, and therefore, long wave communication can still be depended upon to operate reliably at slow speeds

under conditions when short wave working may be temporarily interrupted. Telegraphy effected by the use of
long waves did not constitute by itself a really serious competition with cable communication, whereas the introduction
of short wave beam wireless, in spite of its limitations as
regards constant all day working, has, on account of its
reliability during the hours when it is effective on a circuit,
and due to the very high speed of working, and its consequent
great commercial capacity, proved itself such a very serious
rival to cable communication as to bring about a merging
of the interests of both Cable and Wireless operations.
Long wave communication under its special limitations,
although expensive, is still necessary to a wireless telegraph
organization, and will remain so until further investigation
has discovered means of ensuring a greater continuity of
short wave wireless communication under all conditions.
This particular problem is so far from being solved that at
the present time the British Post Office, for their important
telephone service with America, and the Imperial and
International Communications Ltd., for their services with
America and the more distant points in Europe, have
recently built new long wave stations to supplement their
existing means of communication. The development of
the technique of long wave wireless installations in recent
years has been to limit the radiation of harmonics, and
ensure constancy of the frequency of the emitted wave.
The employment of long waves in the future is not likely
to increase in the sphere of wireless point to point communication, and little development in the technique of this
branch is probable, but in the field of broadcasting transmission, where " medium " and " long " waves are utilized,
and where more and more powerful broadcasting transmitters are being installed, continuous development takes
place, and the improvements made, and experience gained
in the broadcasting field, will equally apply to future designs
of long wave transmitters, should they still be required to
supplement the services carried out by short wave stations.

When the Imperial wireless beam stations were constructed
they were the first of this new form of communication, and
the whole short wave spectrum was available in which to

choose the wavelengths most likely to give the best results for the various services. Two wavelengths were selected for each service, one for day and one for night communication, and the wavelengths thus selected were chosen to be about 40,000 cycles apart to ensure no possible difficulties by mutual interference. Furthermore, the receivers were designed to respond to a wave band of about 10,000 cycles to ensure that, should there be any variation or drift in the receiving circuits, or in the frequency of the transmitted wave within the wide limits of 10,000 cycles, the receiver would still be responsive to the signals without constant adjustment.

The risks that the Marconi Company were taking in accepting and carrying out a contract for Imperial wireless communications under most stringent guarantees, based entirely on the confidence created by their own pioneer investigations, and on Marconi's profound conviction, as the result of his preliminary experiments, were still so great that the engineers responsible were justified in eliminating all unnecessary risks which could be foreseen. The instantaneous and remarkable success of beam communication caused an immediate revolution in the technique of wireless. All operating organizations and companies who were effecting wireless services by the long wave system either adopted the beam system as devised by the Marconi Company or designed other types of beam aerials to effect equivalent results, and short wave stations, with or without directive aerials, were rapidly constructed in all parts of the world. It was soon seen that if some system of international regulation were not enforced the multiplication of short wave wireless stations, substituting the less efficient long wave stations, and the creation of many new stations, working on short waves, for all classes of services, and in most cases using at least two wavelengths, would soon cause such a congestion in the limited useful band of the spectrum that chaotic conditions of affairs would arise and many services be liable to be interfered with by other stations, no matter how distant, working on or near the same wavelength. This was therefore one of the most important subjects dealt with at the International Conference held in Washington in 1927. At this Conference

certain regulations were laid down. The effective band of
the spectrum was divided up into sections, and the different
sections were specifically allocated to different services. Some
sections, distributed through the spectrum, were exclusively
reserved for services between fixed points, others for mobile
services, such as ships at sea and aircraft, others for broadcasting, while the interests of amateur experimentalists were
safeguarded by the provision of definite bands reserved for
their exclusive use. It was further agreed at the Conference
that " The width of band of frequencies, occupied by the
emission of a station, must correspond reasonably with
technical progress for the type of communication concerned,"
also " Where bands of frequencies are assigned to a special
service, the stations engaged in each service must use frequencies which are sufficiently remote from the limits of such
bands not to produce serious interference with the working
of stations engaged in services to which the immediately
adjacent bands of frequencies are allotted."

The Conference did not definitely specify the width of band
that might be considered reasonable for any particular frequency, but all Administrations were aware of the difficulty
of ensuring constancy of the emitted frequency, and the
necessity of a degree of tolerance.

Many proposals were considered officially and unofficially
to arrive at some agreed method of determining the width of
band allowable. One proposal was made that the width of
band allowed to any station should be the figure obtained by
taking the square root of ten times the frequency. Thus a
station working on a wavelength of 15 metres, or 20,000 kilocycles, would be allocated a band width of approximately
14 kilocycles, while a station with a wavelength of 30 metres,
or 10,000 kilocycles, would be allocated a band width of
10 kilocycles, and a station with a wavelength of 300 metres,
or 1000 kilocycles, would have a band width of a little over
3 kilocycles. This proposal was on scientific lines and had
much to recommend it : it would be easy to alter the multiplying factor to another figure than ten at a later date when
further restrictions might be found necessary. Another proposal put forward was that the width of allowable band should
be a percentage allowance of the frequency used. Neither

of these proposals had general acceptance, and it was finally tacitly and unofficially agreed by the exploiting administrations who discussed the subject at Washington, that they would try to fit their applications for the registrations to allow of a band of not less than 10 kilocycles separation from previously registered wavelengths in the band up to 40 metres. It was realized that the arrangements proposed were not ideal, but it was an endeavour to create some sort of order out of chaos, and that it was in the interests of all wireless operating organizations to avoid as far as possible causing interference to each other.

While the Conference divided up the whole spectrum, used in wireless from the very long waves down to the shortest waves used at the date of the Conference, the only sections with which it is necessary to concern ourselves are those below 175 metres.

The actual division of the spectrum from 175 metres downwards into different sections, and the allocation of these bands to the different services is set forth in Table I of the Appendix. Table II in the Appendix gives the bands restricted to fixed services and Table III the additional bands that can be used by fixed services but which other services have the right to share.

Stations carrying out long distance services require at least two wavelengths. Short wave communication over long distances is effected due to the short waves being reflected from the "Heaviside" layer in the upper atmosphere back to earth. The height of the reflective layer in the atmosphere is dependent on the degree of electronic ionization. The effect of the sun's rays is to increase the depth of the ionization of the upper atmosphere, and the reflective layer is therefore nearer the earth in daytime than in darkness. The longer the daylight path a wave has to travel the shorter must be the wave, within limits, to carry the distance. Hence stations require one wave for daylight communication and another for night.

Experience has shown that even two waves are not enough for communication throughout the twenty-four hours, and to meet summer and winter conditions. Again, it appears that the optimum wavelengths for daylight and night conditions vary according to the degree of magnetic disturbance in the sun. Stations carrying on services north to south, or vice versa, can maintain communication more easily and more consistently with fewer wavelengths than is the case with services in an east to west direction, as north and south communication is not affected by magnetic disturbances to anything like the same degree.

The cycle of solar magnetic activity is about eleven years, and experience shows that shorter waves are more suitable when magnetic storms are prevalent, than in periods of solar quiescence. For example, during the early experiments on short wave working, before the beam stations had been built, it appeared that a wavelength of about 30 metres was the best for daylight communication across the Atlantic, whereas a wave of about 60 metres was best in the hours of darkness. By the time the beam stations were completed the 32 metre wave was found to be a satisfactory night wave, while a 16 metre wave was found to be the most suitable at that date for day working. By 1931 conditions on the transatlantic circuit had substantially changed, and the 32 metre wave now often gets through by day and is frequently unsatisfactory by night, whereas a longer wave about 60 meters, or even longer, is now required at night, particularly in the dark hours of the winter months. The wavelengths found most useful on this circuit in the winter of 1931–1932 are a day wave of about 22 metres, which generally fades out about sunset in England, followed by a wavelength of about 40 metres for six or eight hours, after which a wavelength of 75 metres is used. The indications are that an even longer wave than 75 metres would be beneficial in the hours of intense winter darkness ; sometimes a wavelength around 57 metres was found to carry through the service from about 8 p.m. up to noon the next day, that is, well into daylight conditions. Hour to hour, and day to day, observations taken at the Somerton receiving station of Imperial and International Communications Ltd., where reception is effected from New York on a number of different wavelengths, and which is also the receiving centre for the South American, Japanese, Egyptian and other circuits, tend to prove that all wireless conditions definitely go through a monthly cycle, apparently due to the rotation of the sun on its axis. This seems to indicate that the solar radiation varies in intensity from different parts of the sun's surface. This monthly cyclic change is distinct from the eleven year cycle of solar magnetic activity. Careful records have been kept of the varying conditions on all long distance wireless circuits, and a great deal has been learned, but until a full cycle of eleven years of solar activity has passed, and the changing effects noted, it will not be possible to determine definitely what are the optimum wavelengths on each circuit, day by day, and year by year.

It can be seen therefore that at least two wavelengths, and in certain cases more, are necessary on important long distance circuits. Even so, on certain particularly difficult routes, the use at different times of the day and at different seasons of four or five wavelengths has not rendered the circuit completely satisfactory.

It will be of interest to study a table showing the approximate number of wavelengths registered by the end of 1931 in each band, taken from the last published Berne International List. Table IV in the Appendix sets out the bands of wavelengths allocated to fixed services, the theoretical number of wavelengths available, again on the arbitrary assumption of a ten thousand separation cycle, and the number of allocations of wavelengths in each band to fixed stations.

Table V shows the number of wavelengths already registered by fixed and mobile stations in the shared band.

From these tables it is apparent that by the beginning of 1932 there were already registered over 3500 wavelengths for stations carrying out point to point services, while there was only room for 1037 stations if each had a world range, and each had the exclusive right to a registered wavelength with a band width of 10,000 cycles. In the shared band there is only room for 541 stations, both fixed and mobile, with the same exclusive wavelength separation, yet already nearly 3000 have been registered.

The position is, however, not so serious as these figures indicate. A large number of the stations which have been allocated wavelengths utilize very small power in the aerial, and carry on only an intermittent service. Some fixed stations utilize wavelengths in the daytime for services over comparatively short distances, which only carry long distance by night. Furthermore, a very considerable number of wavelengths have been registered by certain countries for stations which have never been erected.

In Table VI of the Appendix the various bands of frequencies reserved for point to point services are again set forth, with a column giving the approximate number of wavelength allocations, registered at Berne by the end of 1931, and further columns are shown in which the total registered allocations have been split up according to the power in kilowatts used by these stations.

It will be seen that no less than 1115 out of a total of 3554 allocations use power of under ½ kilowatt, 391 use powers of 2 kilowatts or under, and of the 664 where the power has not been recorded in the Berne List, or where the stations are not yet erected, a very large proportion are intended for local or interior services, and can be reckoned to come in the list of stations with output under 2 kilowatts. It can therefore be safely stated that about 2000 out of the total of 3554 allocations are unlikely to cause serious interference with more distant services. It will be noticed that there is a large number of allocations for stations using power to the aerial of over 50 kilowatts. Here again the figures, on analysis, convey a wrong impression. Certain organizations, particularly wireless operating companies in the U.S.A., register the same wavelength several times over, in cases where stations to which the wavelength is allotted carry out more than one service. Furthermore they frequently register the same wavelength to two or more of their stations, in order that each station can act as a reserve or alternative to the other. To make a complete analysis of these subdivisions in Table VI and attempt to arrive at the actual number of wavelengths in each section that are likely to be in operation at the same time would occupy too much space. Enough has been given to indicate the existing position as regards their congestion.

Much attention has been given in the past few years to the stabilization of the frequency of the emitted wave and stations, except for special services, can work much more closely together than previously thought practicable. The number of new stations built will however go on increasing, and it is clear that the congestion in the ether is getting so severe that, unless steps are taken to enable stations to work still more closely together without interference, the extension of existing services and the inauguration of new services will cause a steady deterioration in the quality of the services at present being rendered, owing to increasing interference.

The situation of wavelength congestion has been dealt with at some length in order to emphasize the importance of research and development work being continuously and systematically undertaken to relieve the congestion. Wireless organizations are fully aware of the position, and during the past few years many research workers have been devoting their attention to the problem. This is being attacked in several different directions, all with a view to utilizing as small a portion of the ether as will give the required signal.

The most obvious and pressing need at the moment is the definite stabilization of frequency control. Much progress has recently been made in this direction and constant frequency drives, or master oscillators, of various types have been designed which have substantially improved the situation, and have ensured that stations in which these drives have been installed keep more nearly to the registered frequency allotted them.

In another chapter reference has been made to the research work carried out in the Marconi Company's laboratories by Mr. G. M. Wright, in developing a master oscillator on the tuning fork principle : other workers have developed the crystal type of master oscillator to a high degree of reliability, while C. S. Franklin has developed a thermionic valve drive which is self compensating for temperature, and which gives a remarkable degree of constancy of frequency to the transmitter to which it is attached, but as yet the final solution has not been completely obtained, and until a degree of accuracy of at least one in one hundred thousand can always be relied upon the Research Engineers have not solved the problem. When it has been solved, and a very high degree of constancy of frequency on commercial wireless stations thereby assured, other methods of reducing the band width of wavelength taken by a transmitter can be utilized, and single side band working on short waves will then be possible, thus doubling the number of stations possible without mutual interference.

Other directions in which developments in wireless telegraph communication between fixed points can be foreseen comprise a more extensive use of directive methods of transmission and reception, thus concentrating the energy transmitted to the required direction, and at the receiving station eliminating interference from other directions. When the beam stations were first put into operation they utilized continuous waves, but experience soon showed that if the wave be slightly modulated most of the rapid momentary fading of signals was eliminated, and the signals were thus much more reliable and faster speeds could be worked. Of course, modulating the wave increases the width of band emitted to the extent of the modulation, and it may be found advisable to revert to continuous waves without modulation, in which case " diversity " reception, first demonstrated by Beverage in America, would be necessary.

Other possible methods are to utilize frequency modulations or to employ phase modulation. All these ideas are being investigated by different workers in the field of wireless research. The necessity for reducing interference and limiting the space occupied in the ether by any one emission is obvious and it can be confidently predicted that a solution will be found.

Mention has already been made of the investigations that are continuously being carried out on the propagation of short waves, and the periodic variation in the optimum length of wave required for any particular communication. Many scientific workers have been studying the effect of sunspots on electro-megnetic radiation. T. L. Eckersley has written a number of valuable papers on the reflection of short waves from the Heaviside layer and the effects of magnetic disturbances. The result of such scientific investigation is of the greatest assistance in determining the optimum wave necessary, and the minimum number of waves required for any commercial service. It is from the work of such scientists and investigators that already it can be determined in advance what wave to use for any new service.

Other problems on which research and development work are indicated comprise improvements in methods of signalling, the elimination of mechanical devices, such as the Wheatstone transmitter by light operated relays, and the extension of the use of the regenerator and cable code working on wireless circuits, whereby secrecy of communication is to a great extent assured, and by means of which a reduction in operating expenses can be effected. When it is realized that the salaries of operators on a wireless circuit amounts to no less than 47 per cent of the total cost of the service every device which tends to reduce the human element in the handling of traffic is of the utmost commercial importance.

As regards methods of signalling it is probable that channel signalling will be further developed, so that separate messages can be transmitted on a circuit with frequencies differing from each other by only a few hundred cycles. The importance of secrecy is likely to be emphasized in the telegraphic, as well as the telephonic, side of communications. The fact that traffic on short wave beam circuits passes at speeds requiring automatic methods of recording in itself gives a certain degree of immunity from interception, but the most promising method of secret telegraphy is the application of the Cable Code and Regenerator system devised by the technical staff of the Cable Companies to wireless circuits. This method involves the mixing of two or more messages on one channel, and their subsequent selection at the receiving end. Morse code is not used, the dots and dashes being all of equal length. A most ingenious mechanical device has been designed, known as the Regenerator, which restores the signals to their proper shape. Synchronization between transmitter and receiver is automatically effected. This system has been installed on the England-South Africa circuit with marked success. Not only does this method ensure a very high degree of secrecy, but it also is effective in economy of staff, and in reduction of errors and consequent repetitions. The experience gained on the South African circuit points to its extended use on other circuits.

Developments in methods of direct printing of messages

on wireless channels, in order to reduce handling costs, are also probable. The cable code system referred to does effect this, but other methods of direct printing are being investigated and tried out.

The tendency in modern commercial practice is to reduce the size of the transmitting and receiving aerials as much as possible. The original beam aerials for the Imperial stations were perhaps more extensive than necessary for the service they were required to effect, but there is a danger that, in order to keep costs down as much as possible, the aerials may be reduced not only in width but in height also. Height has an important function in narrowing the width of the total angle of incidence in the vertical field, and so forms the best safeguard against distortion due to secondary signals arriving at the aerial from high angles. The probable development in aerial design will be on the lines of simple beam aerials at the transmitting stations, their width and height depending upon the nature of the service they are required to perform, but at the receiving station it is probable that some form of diversity reception will be found necessary. By diversity reception is meant simultaneous reception on more than one receiver, connected to separate aerials, spaced at distances of the order of ten wavelengths apart. In this case on the important busy circuits it would be best to erect three separate directive aerials, on the diversity principle, with perhaps a rather wide angle of incidence in the horizontal field.

Beam aerials give remarkable freedom from interference, due to their directive properties and large receptive powers, but the economics of commercial wireless, covering services of secondary as well of primary importance, calls for cheaper aerial systems. Such cheapening can now be effected without degrading the signal to interference ratio, but the level of strength of signal is reduced, necessitating increased amplification in the receivers.

As regards receiver design, the limit to amplification in a receiver, after all precautions in circuit design have been taken, is determined by the valves used. Very great strides have been made already in the reduction of valve " hiss " which modulates to a greater or less extent any signal which the valve is called upon to amplify. With sufficient valves in cascade, however, the last valve of a receiver will be overloaded by valve noise, emanating from the first valve, and the noiseless amplification obtainable will depend on still further improvements in valve design.

The design of receivers for commercial services is governed to a certain extent by the type of receiving aerial employed. The enormous increase in the number of stations operating in the short wave band from 15 to 60 metres calls for increased selectivity in the receiver without, however, restricting the band of frequencies essential to the particular type of transmission required. Different types of receivers are required therefore for telegraphy, telephony, facsimile or picture telegraphy, broadcast reception, and television.

The design of receiving arrangements should aim at reducing the band width of frequencies which it is necessary to transmit in order to effect sufficiently high class communication in each of these services, as well as to benefit by the reduction of band width made possible by improvements in transmitter design. The general adoption of diversity aerials at the receiving stations would avoid the necessity for the audio frequency modulation of telegraph transmitters, a system which seriously increases the band width transmitted. The old bugbear of short wave working was continual variation of the transmitter frequency, which necessitated extra band width in the receiving filters. In all modern transmitters various types of constant frequency drives have enabled such constancy to be attained that the onus for stability now rests with the receiving heterodyne, and the inconstancy of the transmitter no longer requires extra band width in the receiver.

Future receivers will require to have their heterodyne stabilized in like manner to the transmitter if advantage is to be taken of the small margin of band width made possible by transmitter improvements. Heterodynes of such stability, but continuously variable over a wide range of wavelengths, present serious difficulties in design, but it is this same component which requires perfecting before " single side band " working on short waves can be feasible.

Other tendencies in receiver design include the introduction of devices for limiting the strength of signals in order to suppress the effects of secondary signals ; the provision of automatic level controls, as used in telephone receivers, and measuring devices for determining the gain in each circuit.

As regards transmitters, the elimination of all batteries, and the provision of rectifiers for all circuits, is the latest trend in transmitter design, whilst the necessity of using more than one wavelength on a circuit has emphasised the importance of means whereby the wavelength of a transmitter can be rapidly changed. The importance of the constancy of the frequency of the transmitter has already been emphasised.

An endeavour has been made to give an idea as to the lines along which progress will proceed. Scientists and research workers as a rule put forward what in their opinion will give the best results, regardless of the cost, and generally they are not directly interested in the economics of engineering. It is therefore for the practical engineer to weigh up the advantages and disadvantages of any new proposal, and to strike a fair mean. He may be attacked by the research engineer for not having given sufficient consideration to the advantages that would be obtained if the proposal put forward was adopted without any departure from it, and he will probably be open to criticism from the financial side of his business, whatever action he recommends, for the cost of the proposal, but economics govern development and compromise is the only way to ensure progress, though rate of progress may thereby appear to be retarded.

PLATE XV

SIR AMBROSE FLEMING, F.R.S.
The inventor of the thermionic valve

[face p. 199

CHAPTER XVIII

BROADCASTING—DEVELOPMENT

BROADCASTING, by which we mean the reproduction at a distance of speech and music, necessitates the production at the transmitting station, and the emission from the aerial of a continuous wave of pure sinusoidal form. This wave travels out in all directions, and forms the aethereal bridge which provides the passage for the electrically converted sounds from the studio to the receiver. The frequency of these continuous waves varies inversely to the wavelength. In the case of ordinary broadcasting stations, which have wavelengths allocated to them varying from 200 metres to 545 metres, the frequency of these waves varies from one million five hundred thousand to five hundred and fifty thousand vibrations a second, according to the actual wavelength used, and they travel always at the same speed as light, 186,000 miles a second, from the transmitting aerial. On this continuous stream of pure waves is superimposed the electrical reproduction of the sound waves created in the studio. These sound waves, which are detectable by the human ear, are of much lower frequency, ranging from thirty vibrations a second in the case of the lowest audible notes, such as the beat of a drum, to vibrations of 10,000 or even 15,000 a second, in the case of the harmonics of the higher notes of music which determine the perfection of its reproduction. The superimposition of these constantly varying low frequency waves of most complex form upon the carrier wave create new wave forms, in which the carrier wave becomes a component part. The importance of the purity of form of the original carrier wave is therefore evident, since any variation from the pure sine shape would cause distortion in the reproduction at the receiver of the sounds carried.

In wireless telegraphy it was not essential to generate continuous waves in order to transmit a signal from one place to another, and it was only shortly before the war that continuous wave transmission began to be made use of commercially in long distance wireless telegraphy. A number of different devices were invented for generating continuous waves. Poulsen invented an arc transmitter, based on Duddell's discovery in 1900 that a carbon electric arc is capable of generating electric oscillations, and the production of continuous oscillations by this means at once led to attempts to conduct telephony by modulating the amplitude of these waves by a microphone. The difficulty of maintaining, and particularly of modulating, a pure and steady wave prevented this method being of any practical commercial success, although wireless telephony was actually effected by this means. After this invention a number of different types of revolving machines were invented, such as Marconi's timed disc and the high frequency alternators, invented by Alexanderson in America, Latour in France, and Goldschmidt in Germany. All of these were used in commercial wireless telegraph stations with success but the wave form they emitted, while continuous, was not sinusoidal, and not suitable for distortionless telephony. The master invention of the thermionic valve by Sir Ambrose Fleming and the subsequent invention by Dr. Lee de Forest in the U.S.A. of the three-electrode valve, and the later discovery that the valve could be utilized as a generator of oscillations, as well as an amplifier or detector, rendered all other methods of creating continuous oscillations obsolete and made telephony by wireless and broadcasting possible. The invention of the thermionic valve is a most striking example of a vast industry owing its origin to an intelligent investigation of an obscure effect, undertaken merely from scientific curiosity.

In the early days of the development of the ordinary incandescent electric lamp Edison noted that the bulb became blackened on the inside as the lamp was used, but that there was a line of glass free from discolouration in the plane of the filament loop. To investigate this effect Edison suspended a metal plate inside the bulb near the filament. He found that when the plate was connected to the positive terminal of a battery an electric current passed, although there was an apparent open circuit as the filament and plate in the

PLATE XVI

[By permission of The Exclusive News Agency

DR LEE DE FOREST

bulb were insulated from each other, whereas if the negative terminal of the battery were connected to the plate no current passed. Edison published this result in 1883. Fleming was also investigating the cause of the blackening of lamps and published his observations in 1883 in a paper on " Molecular Radiation in Incandescent Lamps." The phenomenon became generally of interest to physicists, and other investigators, among them Elster and Geitel in Germany, published the results of their investigations. Fleming, in particular, made a very thorough investigation of the phenomenon and as a result of his investigations between 1889 and 1896 concluded that negative electricity was in some way given off by incandescent carbon and platinum filaments. In 1897 Sir Joseph Thomson made the great discovery that the atom was not incapable of being divided, as hitherto believed, but was built up of still smaller units of electricity called electrons. From this followed the discovery that the incandescent filament in a lamp is continuously sending out vast numbers of electrons in all directions. In 1903 another physicist in England, O. W. Richardson, propounded his well-known formula showing that the relation of the quantity of electrons emitted is dependent on the temperature of the emitting substance. All these investigations were published but no one except Fleming saw the possibility of utilizing the effect for the detection of wireless signals. Fleming during his investigations on the possibility of rectifying alternating currents of high frequency recalled to mind his early experiments on the Edison effect, and placed a metal cylinder around the filament to catch the negative stream of electrons and to see whether this could not therefore act as a rectifier of high frequency oscillations. The experiment was a complete success and the two electrode valve, or the " oscillation valve," which was the name given to the instrument by Dr. Fleming, came into being. It was found to be a reliable form of detector of electric waves and was introduced forthwith into the Marconi transatlantic receiving stations.

Three years passed before the next important stage in valve development took place. In 1907 Dr. Lee de Forest made an important invention by inserting a third electrode, known as a grid, between the filament and the plate, thereby making it possible to amplify the feeble oscillations, as well as to rectify and detect them.   Years passed before the capabilities of three electrode valves were thoroughly appreciated and that by coupling the grid and plate circuits together in a particular way it was also capable of acting as a generator of high frequency oscillations.   This discovery was made practically simultaneously by Dr. Meissner in Germany, Franklin in England, and Armstrong in U.S.A. This invention was the birth of the transmitting valve and at once rendered wireless telephony possible, as the amplitude of these oscillations so generated could be controlled, in many different ways, by a microphone.   Unlike the continuous waves produced by alternators and other means, they are pure in form and can be modulated without distortion.   A new industry was created, and thermionic valves for different purposes were manufactured in large quantities. In 1915 American wireless engineers built a transmitter using no fewer than 300 thermionic valves and succeeded in transmitting speech from the United States to Paris. In 1919, after the war, Capt. Round transmitted speech during daylight from Ireland to Canada, using only 2·5 kilowatts with a wavelength of 3800 metres.   About this time the idea sprang up of broadcasting music, news, and speeches to the general public.   This idea started in America and at once took hold of the imagination.   A new art, and a huge industry, was thus created.   A great impetus was given to valve design and construction, and it became evident that much more powerful valves would be necessary.   Valves have gradually increased in size and in several broadcasting stations in Europe there are now valves in use rated at 100 kilowatts.   Valves have recently been manufactured of a rating as high as 500 kilowatts and the employment of the thermionic valve as a generator of continuous waves has now become universal, superseding all previous devices.

The thermionic valve formed the bridge whereby the signals sent out from the transmitting station were conveyed to the receiver, but more was wanted.   The microphone, with which every user of a telephone is familiar, was not developed to the degree necessary for the perfect reproduction of the infinitely varying graduations of music.   It could convert intelligibly the sounds created by speech so that they would be understood by the listener in, but in the finer graduations of music quality suffered. Much research work was devoted to improvements in microphone design, to discover a means of creating a true response to all vibrations of sound, from the lowest to the highest frequencies to which the ear is sensitive, before the quality of transmission that is now demanded could be attained. Novelty covers a multitude of sins, and if the quality of the performance of the early days of broadcasting, which then brought in large quantities of congratulatory letters, were reverted to on one programme at the present time, the public would demand the resignation of the whole personnel of the B.B.C.

On the receiving side great developments have taken place in many directions, especially in simplicity of control. The biggest development in this direction, however, has been in the improvement of loud speakers. In the early days of broadcasting the best loud speaker was only responsive to a small band of the frequencies necessary for the proper reproduction of music, and even now there is much room for improvement.

It is impossible to give even a brief history of the development of the art of broadcasting in a single chapter ; to deal with the subject would require several volumes. Many books have, however, been written on the subject of broadcasting, and for those interested in its early history no better book can be recommended than *Wireless and Broadcasting*, by Mr. Arthur Burrows. For general information on broadcasting readers are recommended to buy the *B.B.C. Year Book*. On the technical side there are numerous books available, several by Capt. P. P. Eckersley, and a number of admirable technical papers have been read before the Institution of Electrical Engineers, which have been published by the Institution : in addition to this the wireless broadcasting public is able to keep up to date by reading the *Wireless World, World Radio*, and other wireless periodicals.

The boom in broadcasting started in America in 1920. The first regular broadcasting station in the United States was built by the Western Electric and Manufacturing Company at East Pittsburg, and is the station well known under the call letters KDKA. Newspapers and big retail stores soon saw that broadcasting offered a wonderful opportunity for advertising their wares. Unlike Great Britain, there were no regulations which forbade this, and the number of broadcast stations privately owned by shops and stores rapidly increased. It did not matter whether one station were interfering with another in those days : there was a boom in broadcasting, and everyone was going to get in on the aether. By the middle of 1923 there were over 500 broadcasting stations in America and an audience of about 2 million. By 1924 the number of stations had grown to 1105, and the 89 wavelengths available had to be shared by them ; chaos in the aether was of course the result. Great Britain was slow to start on general broadcasting. The restrictions imposed on private activities in England, while frequently annoying, are generally for the public good, and in wireless matters the British Post Office invariably investigate a new proposal thoroughly before sanctioning it, a procedure which in this case has been greatly to the advantage of all listeners.

American practice showed the danger of unrestricted control, and the necessity of confining the transmission of programmes to one authority. At the start of broadcasting in England the Post Office granted permission to a few experimenters to use small transmitters not exceeding 10 watts capacity, but they were only allowed to send music for purposes of test. In 1921, after many discussions, the Post Office authorized a very limited broadcasting to be carried out from the Marconi Company research station at Writtle, near Chelmsford, with a station limited to 200 watts. The number of listeners in were few, but the concerts, for the most part from gramophone records or provided by the staff at the Chelmsford Works who had some musical talent, were much appreciated. In 1922 the Post Office took a more sympathetic attitude to broadcasting and greater facilities were granted. A station was built at Marconi House, and by the autumn the number of licences taken out had increased from a few hundred to about thirty thousand. Other organizations besides the Marconi Company were interested in broadcasting and were permitted to build stations. Conflicting interests eventually brought about an agreement to form a British Broadcasting Company, financed by these various interests, but under severe restrictions, wisely imposed by the Post Office. The British Broadcasting Company was not allowed to use the stations for advertisement, and the maximum dividend they might pay was limited to $7\frac{1}{2}$ per cent. The Company was given a definite licence until the end of 1926, and Major Reith, now Sir John Reith, was appointed Managing Director. Shortly afterwards Captain P. P. Eckersley, whose personality had become so well known for the able and amusing way he had conducted the early broadcasting programmes from the original Writtle station, was appointed Chief Engineer. British Broadcasting was now definitely launched and under the able control of Major Reith (now Sir John Reith), it has become a model to other countries of how a broadcasting organization should be conducted. The number of stations erected in Great Britain grew to meet the needs of the public and in order to serve all districts. Wireless broadcast technique rapidly advanced, both in the factory and studio. Transmitters were made of larger and larger power, while special attention was given to all details likely to improve technical performance. In 1926 the British Broadcasting Company's licence expired, and its connection with various commercial businesses ceased, and it was reconstructed as an independent Corporation, under Sir John Reith as Director-General.

Space will not permit of a description of the gradual growth in technical development, but it is necessary to point out the increasing difficulties with which those responsible for the technical development have to contend, due to the restriction in the band of frequencies allotted by International regulations to broadcasting, and to the serious interference caused by the ever increasing power of the European broadcasting stations. The International Conference at Washington in 1927 allocated certain bands of frequencies to various services. The needs of every type of service had to be considered, but the fundamental needs of shipping, since wireless was its only means of communication, had to receive first consideration.

Wireless on board ship had been established since the beginning of the century and over 15,000 ships had been fitted. The wavelength for intercommunication with ships and for distress calls had been for many years 600 metres, and it was not desirable to change this. Broadcasting was a newcomer and had not in 1927 developed to its present magnitude. It was therefore allocated a band of wavelengths below 600 metres and sufficiently removed from that band not to be interfered with or to cause interference to shipping. A band from 200 to 545 metres was given, equivalent to 1500 to 550 kilocycles. A few longer waves were allowed to certain existing European stations, among which was Daventry, but the main difficulty in European broadcasting has been to avoid mutual interference due to the narrowness of the medium wave band allocated to accommodate all European stations. International cooperation therefore between the broadcast organizations of European nations became essential if chaos were to be avoided, and an international broadcasting union was formed, which by private agreement allocated the available band of frequencies to the different nations.

A meeting was held in Geneva at which 10 kilocycles was considered to be the minimum safe separation between stations to avoid interference. At a subsequent meeting of the various administrations at Prague, it became necessary to divide the broadcast band into 106 channels to accommodate all the stations the various European countries had either built or were building, and it was necessary to reduce the separation to 9 kilocycles. Of the 106 channels, 95 were exclusively allotted, 11 being common waves, to be available to any nation for small stations of small range.

The degree of success in any scheme of wavelength allocation must be judged only as it affects the listener at his local station. The wavelengths were parcelled out on the principle that nearby stations should, as far as possible, have wavelengths widely separated, and that contiguous wavelengths should be allocated to widely separated stations. The Prague scheme undoubtedly reduced the interference previously experienced but the continual increase in the number of stations erected, and more particularly the continuous increase in the power of stations, and their consequent range, have increased the difficulties of the Broadcasting Authorities and caused a falling off in the quality of reception, due to mutual interference.

In 1929 there was a total of 200 broadcasting stations in Europe, including 11 in Russia, having a combined power of 600 kilowatts. Two years later the number of stations had increased to 261, including 48 in Russia, and their combined power had swollen to 2860 kilowatts. Several stations are now working with powers of 120 kilowatts to the aerial, and over 30 stations have a carrier wave power of 50 kilowatts or more, whereas at the time of the Prague Conference there were only four such stations.

It is not difficult to explain the reasons which have led to the growth in the size of broadcasting stations.

Wireless waves have no regard for frontiers and no tariff wall can keep them out. In some instances listeners near the frontier of their country can actually receive more satisfactorily the concerts from a neighbouring country than the programmes from their own national stations. In addition to this many people derive a peculiar satisfaction in receiving foreign stations, even when the foreign station can only give them music of an indifferent quality, owing to the long range, rather than in listening to the local programmes of excellent quality from their own national station. No Government can be indifferent to the fact that many of its nationals can receive foreign stations more satisfactorily than their own, and the result has been a constant demand for more and more powerful stations, and increased range within the limits possible with the wavelength allotted. Every increase of power of broadcasting transmitters in one country leads to a similar or larger increase in the power of the stations of its neighbours, and so the evil goes on, and so it will continue until by the severe pressure of the great international body of listeners the various Governments will be forced to take action to reduce the interference. In England the B.B.C., in order to ensure that every part of Great Britain should be adequately served, and owing to the shortage of wavelengths, developed a system of synchronization, by means of which it has successfully operated eleven stations simultaneously on the same wavelength. This has been made possible by the development of tuning fork control of frequency constancy, and the constancy is maintained to about five parts in one million. Research work on improving this high level of constancy is still being carried out and there is every prospect that this figure will shortly be further substantially reduced.

Chapter XIX

BROADCASTING—PRESENT DAY PROBLEMS

THE growth of power of broadcasting stations has greatly increased interference to distant stations. The practical service range of a station is determined by the range of the direct ray which has travelled over the surface of the earth, and can deliver a signal of requisite strength above noise level to a good quality receiver. The broadcasting waves are not confined to direct rays, but are emitted as high angle rays also, and these are reflected down from the ionized layers in the upper atmosphere, to return to earth at distances outside the service area of the station. Interference is caused by the high value of signal strength of the indirect ray at considerable distances from the broadcast station. The shorter the wavelength transmitted the greater the relative value of the indirect ray. These indirect rays in the broadcast band are not reflected in daylight, but serious interference is caused after sunset. Unfortunately an increase in the power of a transmitter using the shorter waves of the broadcast band does not increase the range of the direct ray to the extent that it increases the indirect ray, which is the main cause of the increase in interference. If it were possible to suppress the indirect ray, interference on the local station at night would cease. At the same time listeners would no longer be able to listen to foreign stations, which at present can only be heard at night by virtue of the reflected ray. It has been stated that most transmitters of 50 kilowatts carrier wave power produce, during the hours of darkness, field intensities up to 5 mw. per metre at distances of 600 miles, and unless the spacing between stations can be increased above 9 kilocycles it is difficult to see how the deterioration of broadcast reproduction can effectively be prevented.

A possible remedy to the existing state of interference might be the suppression of the carrier and one side band, thus substantially reducing the separation required to avoid interference, but there are technical difficulties in the application of this method, and the necessity of reproducing the carrier wave at the receiver would increase the complications and costs of the broadcast receiver, and the difficulties of the layman in its operation. The obvious means of relief to the broadcasting services would be by a redistribution of the wavelengths allotted to other services.

Space does not allow of a description of the gradual technical improvements made by the B.B.C. in British broadcasting. All listeners are aware of the latest developments whereby, instead of a number of small stations serving single towns and cities, the B.B.C. decided to build five regional stations, each provided with two transmitters, working on different wavelengths, to serve whole regions of the country, with the choice of two programmes. Most of these stations were completed in 1932. Each transmitter employs 50 kilowatts carrier power to the aerial, and the area they are capable of serving depends on the wavelength used. The B.B.C. has announced its intention of enlarging the Daventry station and 5GB also. When these have been completed Great Britain will be provided with the most up-to-date and technically perfect equipment in the world.

True reproduction of speech or music from the microphone involves the perfection of every detail in the transmitting apparatus. The microphone converts the sounds conveyed to it by air waves into electrical energy, and these feeble electrical impulses are passed through the low frequency amplifiers, where their strength is many times increased. They then pass through the modulator control and modulator, up to the final stages of high frequency power amplifiers, which in turn pass the modulated high frequency carrier oscillations to the aerial.

The microphone has been greatly improved in recent years but it still remains the weakest link in broadcasting transmission. If the microphone does not faithfully reproduce the sounds conveyed to it into equivalent electric currents, or gives greater strength to certain frequencies of sound than to others, then this unfaithful reproduction will be carried through all the stages of the transmitter, through the ether, to the receiver and loud speaker. The important range of frequencies of sound lie between 30 and 10,000 cycles a second. A perfect microphone would give equal response throughout the whole band of these frequencies. No microphone exists at the present day which does this under all conditions ; there is therefore an important field for investigation in improvements in microphone design.

It is not proposed to describe in detail the design or construction of a modern broadcasting transmitter, but only to give an indication of the direction in which broadcasting transmitter technique tends to follow.

The practice of using high power modulation, which was the method usually adopted in the smaller transmitters used in the earlier days of broadcasting, has gradually given way to what is called low power modulation, whereby the high frequency oscillations are modulated at a low power level, that is to say, in one of the early stages of high frequency amplification, and the modulated high frequency oscillations have then to be amplified up to the final stage without distortion. This method is not so simple technically as the method known as high power modulation, but its more obvious advantages have brought it into general use. It eliminates the necessity of high power modulating valves, and the use of iron for transformers working at high power, and if it is desired further to increase the size of the transmitter, another stage of amplification can be added without scrapping the rest of the transmitter. It involves however great care in the design of the high frequency amplifiers, in order to prevent distortion, and this difficulty is emphasized by the ever-growing demand for distortionless modulation, even up to 100 per cent and at the same time the highest possible efficiency and economy of power. This demand has led designers to reduce the number of valves used, by increasing their individual power, and to increase their efficiency by designing the valves to work at higher anode voltages. Valves which are rated at 100 kilowatts input are now in use in a number of high power broadcasting stations, while valves have been manufactured lately of powers up to 500 kilowatts input.

The importance of high efficiency throughout the transmitter without sacrificing performance is another requisite. Many modern stations are now using from 400 to 600 kilowatts of power to the anodes of the valves. Power is expensive, and every step which will reduce the total power taken from the mains for the same radiated energy reduces maintenance costs and is an attractive feature. A considerable wastage of power used to take place in the rectification of the alternating current from the mains into high tension direct current for feeding the valves. The old form of rectifiers had an efficiency not greater than 80 per cent, whereas the introduction of the mercury rectifier of various types has increased the efficiency of rectification to 95 per cent and even higher. Three types of mercury rectifiers are used, the mercury vapour valve developed in America, the glass bulb mercury rectifier, and the mercury arc rectifier contained in a steel cylinder, and kept continuously evacuated of air by means of a vacuum pump. The glass bulb type is largely used in Russia ; the mercury vapour type is preferred in America, and is also installed at the Rome station, while the Mercury Arc Rectifier, as designed by the Brown-Boveri Company, has been installed in Warsaw and many other European stations.

In the design of high power broadcasting stations special precautions have to be taken to prevent the radiation of harmonics. It is becoming the general practice to insert low-pass filters between the output of the transmitter and the aerial feeder circuit, and not only to screen the individual panels of the transmitter but also all the inter-connections of the panels.

Wireless telephony and broadcasting are becoming more and more an exact science. Methods have been devised whereby accurate measurements can be taken of the performance of the transmitter as a whole, and of each individual unit or detail. It is possible to measure the degree of amplification per stage, the depth of modulation and the response curve of each section, and in fact all the salient details which determine the true reproduction of the sound passed to the microphone through the various stages up to and from the aerial.

The acoustical properties of the studio, in which the microphone is placed, have been investigated, since the quality of the sound received at the microphone is obviously determined by the amount of reverberation or echo caused by the size or shape of the studio or the materials of which it is constructed. The B.B.C. has made an exhaustive study of the problem of studio design. In its new headquarters, where no less than 22 different studios have been constructed, each studio has been designed and constructed to meet a particular service, the acoustic properties of each studio differing according to the nature of the service. An extremely interesting description of the acoustical problems involved in studio design and the way in which they have been dealt with is contained in the *Year Book* issued by the B.B.C. for 1932.

Owing to the limitation of the number of wavebands available for broadcasting services, attention has recently been drawn to the possibility of using wavelengths in the ultra short wave band under 9 metres. It is known that the direct ray from a short wave transmitter dies out very quickly, due to absorption, and that it is only the ray reflected from the upper atmosphere which is used for long distance communication. Waves under 9 metres in length do not however get reflected, and therefore if they could be used for local broadcasting services they would not be causing interference to other services in distant countries, nor would they be interfered with, owing to their short range. It appears possible that by their use a strictly local service of very high quality with a range of perhaps not more than 8 to 15 miles may be effected. The B.B.C. is carrying out experiments on these lines and has erected an ultra short wave transmitter on the roof of its new building at Langham Place. The site is a good one but it would have been even better to have erected it at the Crystal Palace. It will be extremely interesting to learn the results of the experiment.

With regard to Receiver design, the deterioration in the quality of reception due to interference from other stations, as a result of the ever-increasing power of broadcasting stations in Europe, has had a marked effect on the circuit design of modern receivers. The present-day tendencies in broadcast receiver design appear to lie in the following directions :—

1. Receivers employing highly selective circuits followed by tone correction.
2. Distortionless detectors.
3. Owing to the increasing number of broadcasting stations on short waves, receivers for wavelengths within the broadcast bands between 14 and 50 metres.
4. The experiments now being carried out by the B.B.C. in England, and by others on the Continent, of local broadcasting on ultra short wavelengths, if successful, will lead to a big market in receivers designed for wavelengths between 5 and 7 metres.

Another development in broadcasting is making rapid progress, viz. the re-diffusion of broadcasting signals over land lines laid on like telephone wires and providing a house to house service. Here there is no necessity for the householder to provide himself with a receiver ; all he wants is a loud speaker, which is hired to him at a weekly or monthly rate, in the same manner as a telephone is supplied. Such re-diffusion services are necessarily confined to congested areas. The principle adopted is to erect two or more high quality receivers in a carefully chosen site outside the town to be served, and to bring the signals over land lines into a central point in the town, where several amplifiers are installed and where the volume of the signals is controlled. From the amplifiers a network of overhead trunk land lines radiate to various points in the town, and these branch again into other pairs, to which the loud speakers in the houses connect. It is usual to arrange for alternative programmes, so that the householder can make his choice. This system has a wide application in Holland and in some other European countries.

Short wave broadcasting, as distinct from ultra short wave broadcasting, is used for braodcasting to great distances. The signals are carried by the ray reflected from the Heaviside (or Appleton) layer. The Marconi Company has been operating a broadcast experimental short wave transmitter for the B.B.C. at the Chelmsford Works for several years past. The type of transmitter used was similar to the transmitters employed in beam telegraph communication, with the exception that a modulating panel had to be provided. The aerial used was a single vertical omni-directional aerial and the transmitter was able to transmit on one wavelength only. Notwithstanding its obvious limitations, the programmes it has sent out have been much appreciated all over the world, although the limit of power of the transmitter, the lack of concentration of energy in any particular direction, and the unsuitability of the wavelength used for reception in some countries, rendered the signals subject to fading. The services provided by this station led to many demands from different portions of the Empire that Empire Broadcasting should be undertaken from England, and the B.B.C. has now put into service a short wave broadcasting station at Daventry, equipped with two transmitters for transmitting on different wavelengths simultaneously and employing directional aerials.

Other short wave transmitters for broadcasting purposes have been set up. The Marconi Company constructed one at the Vatican City for the Pope, which is frequently used for important pronouncements by His Holiness, and from time to time broadcasting programmes have been transmitted on special occasions from the commercial beam telegraph station at Bodmin. The knowledge that has been gained in long distance short wave telegraph communication for several years past, and the records of the experimental broadcasting service from Chelmsford, led the B.B.C. to determine the type of transmitters and aerials necessary for an Empire broadcasting service. The transmitters erected are generally similar to those used on short wave telegraph communication, except that means have to be provided for modulating the carrier wave, but, unlike the majority of telegraph short wave transmitters, as it was clear that several different wavelengths would be necessary, the transmitters are designed for rapid change from one wavelength to another.

A long distance communication by short waves is at times handicapped by quick and also by gradual fading. This is often a drawback on telegraph services, but with elaborate receiving aerial systems and by other means the effects of such fading can be greatly reduced. The cost of such aerial systems would, however, be prohibitive to the individual listener, but would be justifiable for any organization desiring to receive the Empire programmes, and relay them from their local stations. Fading on telephone communication is more troublesome than in the case of telegraphy, as one kind of fading causes distortion, which might not render a telegraph signal unreadable, but would certainly interfere with the quality of telephonic reception.

The slow fading is due to the fact that the ionized layer in the upper atmosphere, from which the waves are reflected, is not constant : the degree of variation in ionization is determined by the intensity of the sun's rays ; at night the ionization gets less and less as darkness becomes more intense, whereas by day the reverse is the case.

Quick fading is somewhat different in character. In the early days of short wave telegraph communication pure continuous waves were transmitted. It was found that, whereas the general level of signal strength was great, the momentary variations in strength were enormous, frequently dropping to such a low value, for perhaps only a quarter of a second, sufficient to cause a letter in a word to drop out or part of a signal comprising a letter to fail. It was found that by modulating the pure continuous wave slightly this type of fading could be largely eliminated. What was then happening was this : if the pure wave of, say, ten million cycles a second were not reflected at the exact receiving point, another wave almost the same length might come in with considerable strength, and by modulating the carrier wave with only 1000 cycles or less a band of waves is formed and radiated and hence reflected, and some portion of that band will reach the receiver at sufficient strength to record signals. Prolonged experience has shown the value of this method, and most telegraph transmitters use slight modulation with marked improvement in communication. Beverage, working in America, solved this problem in a different way. He found that a signal which would be of minimum strength at one place would be quite strong at another position only a few hundred yards away. He therefore devised a method of diversity reception, whereby two or three aerial systems were set at distances of about 10 to 20 wavelengths apart, and the received signals from these aerials were combined. In telephony the difficulty of quick fading is not so easy to overcome. All the waves of modulation together make up the complete telephone reproduction, and if any portion of the complete band is very weak the received signals might be unintelligible. Means can be introduced at the receiving station to minimize this difficulty, but the equipment in general is expensive and out of reach of the individual listener, although some form of auto volume control would help to a certain extent and need not be prohibitive in price.

Empire broadcasting which involves the use of the indirect ray reflected from an unstable mirror, cannot ensure the same quality of reception obtainable from the local broadcasting stations in England, although under stable conditions which often persist for hours together excellent reception may be expected.

The Dominions have the necessary technical facilities and resources for reception, and chains of broadcasting transmitting stations available for the rebroadcasting of the B.B.C. Empire programmes, but it is in the less developed Colonies and out-of-the-way districts where the reception of these programmes will be most appreciated. There is no doubt that many individuals in the Colonies will purchase short wave receivers for direct reception of the English programmes, but the quality of the reception will leave much to be desired. It is possible that in some Colonies the local government may decide to build an adequate receiving station, and either re-broadcast the programme so received, or instal a system of radio re-diffusion over a land line network. Where the local government may not feel justified in incurring such expenditure it is possible that some local Company or organization may be formed to provide such a public service. Whatever methods be adopted, careful study of local receiving conditions will be essential ; the extent of the territory to be served, the distribution of the population in towns or country, local geographical conditions, the prevalence of thunderstorms and atmospherics. All these will have to be carefully considered in order to ensure the best reception and re-distribution of the Empire programme in the most efficient and economical way. The invention and perfection of broadcasting has given to humanity a new method of conveying understanding, an opportunity of breaking down distrust between nations, of appreciating the music, the culture, the moral and intellectual development of other nations. The spoken thoughts of all great minds can be heard by the listeners in their millions, Statesmen, Scientists, Travellers, and the most eminent men of the day, may make contact with the people in their own homes. From a social and educational point of view the value of broadcasting is immeasurable. It has raised the standard of education, musical appreciation, and entertainment, to a new level, and has conveyed the words of the greatest spiritual and moral teachers of the period to the smallest and remotest cottages. The range of broadcasting is international. May it not be hoped that with wise guidance its use will exert a great pacific influence on international relations and that it may be of some assistance in producing a helpful spirit between nations of mutual cooperation in the advancement of civilization ?

Chapter XX

WIRELESS AS A CAREER

I AM constantly asked by parents or guardians to advise them how their boys should be trained to become wireless engineers : the majority inform me that their boys can tune the family receiver to a number of different wireless stations or that they can put a broadcast receiver together and that therefore they already know a great deal about wireless and will obviously be useful as engineers. To the lay mind " Wireless " as a profession conjures up an entirely wrong idea. A large number of otherwise well-informed people imagine that wireless means broadcasting, or else confuse it with the operation of a wireless installation on a ship. People seem to have forgotten, since broadcasting has become so universal, that wireless was in commercial use, for communication between fixed points and ships at sea, for many years before the development of the thermionic oscillating valve rendered the satisfactory reproduction of speech and music practicable ; actually the branch of wireless known as broadcasting is only an offshoot of the main work which a wireless engineer is required to carry out, and although a certain number of wireless engineers are absorbed in the running and maintenance of broadcasting transmission stations, yet if wireless engineering were limited to the care and maintenance of these stations there would be a very restricted field of employment. There is, of course, a large number of manufacturers who make broadcasting receivers, each manufacturer employing one or two specialists as designers, but the whole tendency of the design of broadcasting receivers is towards standardization, from the circuit point of view, and the field offered for employment in this class of work is likewise restricted.

There is another class of applicants for positions as wireless engineers or technical assistants, namely, those who have passed through an engineering college or obtained their certificates at a correspondence school : the ambitions of such applicants vary almost as much as their qualifications, frequently in inverse ratio. Some expect to start at the bottom on very small salaries, while others think that they can command salaries which only years of work will bring within their reach.

The first thing to ascertain is whether the applicant has a real bent for engineering or scientific work ; there is no good entering the profession just to make a living unless he is content to remain always in a very subordinate position. I endeavour to find out if the young man wishes to take up the profession for the love of it, regardless of what salary he may receive, pointing out to him that unless he proves himself to be an exceptionally good man, or has especial good fortune, he is unlikely to arrive at a four figure salary even at the time when he reaches pensionable age. It is important in my opinion to point out the difficulties and disadvantages of the wireless engineering profession to applicants, and particularly to guardians, who seem to think there are plenty of splendid openings in wireless and that wireless is the coming thing, as otherwise many youngsters will be trained for a profession for which they are quite unsuitable, whereas in some other line of work they might have successful careers. Wireless is getting to be a crowded profession, and with the tendency to rationalization, and possible merging of companies into one monopolistic organization, the number of vacancies for engineers will become less and less, whereas the qualifications demanded from a successful applicant will become more and more rigorous. It must also be borne in mind that, if through lack of business or through other causes, the monopolistic company has to reduce its expenditure, and the services of the engineer be unfortunately no longer required, there might be no other opening for his particular knowledge or experience, as there would be in the more general branches of the engineering profession.

It is difficult to lay down a hard and fast standard of attainments necessary in a wireless engineer, as the field covered by the profession is now such a wide one, and a young man who would be unsuitable, for example, as a construction engineer, or to go abroad and supervise the execution of contracts, might have the necessary scientific attainments to become a valuable assistant in research or design work ; in other words, the range of engineering knowledge required nowadays in wireless telegraph and telephone practice is so wide that specialization has become necessary. In the early days of wireless at the end of the last century, when the induction coil was the only transmitter and the coherer receiver was practically the same as the instrument that Marconi first invented, the small group of young engineers or electricians, whom Marconi selected, knew the details of the wireless apparatus thoroughly. Each man was fully capable of erecting the small equipments when called upon to do so, and there was no question then of specialization, although some were more mathematically inclined than others. As the science advanced, particularly after the transatlantic experiments, research and design work became necessary, and the early group of engineers gradually sorted themselves out or were selected for special lines of work. Some, like Franklin, took up research, while others were more interested in the heavier engineering side or in the construction of wireless stations ; others again drifted to the office or contract work, while others preferred the work of maintenance and operation of wireless stations, and so gradually specialization in the engineering side of wireless came about.

Those responsible for the selection of young engineers must therefore consider most carefully their individual qualifications, and the Chief Engineer of a wireless organization must have a sound knowledge of the capabilities of each member of his staff to know whom to employ for each position as it arises. Nowadays, when international competition has become so fierce, and profits have consequently to be cut severely to obtain orders, the employment of an unsuitable engineer to supervise a foreign contract might easily result in the local expenditure exceeding the sum estimated, and thus turn an expected profit into a loss.

The qualifications required, therefore, of an applicant for employment in wireless engineering vary so greatly according to the branch in which he desires to specialize, that it seems advisable to set forth the different branches of engineering work required in a big wireless organization, and the special attainments necessary that an engineer should have in each section of work, in the hope that it will be helpful to young engineers or would-be engineers to select the branch which they may profitably take up. It is necessary to make it clear, however, that an engineer taking a position in one class of engineering work is not necessarily confined to that class of work throughout his career. The wisest course is to get the widest experience, and a good man should endeavour to transfer from one class of work to another in the early years of his employment, especially if he has ambitions towards the administrative posts, where a general, though not necessarily specialized, knowledge and experience in all branches of wireless engineering is essential.

The engineering work of a large wireless organization is divided into a number of sections and sub-sections : the main sections are Research and Development, Design and Manufacturing, the Planning department for complete stations and contracts, Station construction and erection, Maintenance and operation of stations and services, and General administration and Supervision. Not only does a large Wireless Company develop and manufacture apparatus for all kinds of wireless services for the purpose of sale but, where permitted, it may establish its own system of communication by wireless ; as an instance the Marconi Company has built up a wireless network of communications, which now is the property of Imperial and International Communications Ltd., and is the most extensive system of wireless communication in the world.

The Research and Development Section naturally is engaged in experimental research in wireless telegraphy and telephony, and in subjects which may be allied to such work, and the results of such research will lead to the development and design of all forms of apparatus suitable for commercial exploitation ; naturally the men engaged in research work must have, first of all, a very sound knowledge of engineering and physics, and in addition a special knowledge of wireless principles. Engineers suitable for research work are born, not made ; they belong to the class in which all eminent professors and scientists are included. Marconi himself was born in this class, with an inventive and imaginative mind, not content ever to take anything for granted, nor to accept as facts theories propounded by other scientists, however eminent. Marconi, however, was endowed by his good fairy with the further advantage of a sound business instinct, which unfortunately is so lacking in most scientists and research engineers. True research might be described as the study of phenomena which will not necessarily be of any immediate commercial or utilitarian benefit but merely increase the sum of scientific knowledge.

Research work, as understood in commercial companies, is more confined to improvements in existing methods, the invention of new electrical circuits, or optical and acoustic devices. From time to time research engineers, while engaged on other studies, make inventions of fundamental and great commercial importance ; for instance, Franklin during his extensive research into short wave communication, and arising out of his experiments with parabolic reflectors, one of Marconi's earlier inventions, devised the flat grid aerial, world famous as the beam aerial. To take another example, the circuits invented by Round and Wright, in connection with the Bellini-Tosi method of Direction Finding, which were patented, are responsible for the high degree of accuracy to which modern direction finding gear has attained.

In order to get an idea of how diverse the work of a research engineer may be in any one line of investigation, it is of interest to record that in the development of the Marconi Company's facsimile communication apparatus, the method of obtaining constant frequency by tuning fork control was studied. Although the tuning fork has been an established piece of apparatus for many years, it was found that the standard tuning fork as it existed was a most unsuitable piece of apparatus for the control of frequency, and consider-able research work had to be undertaken before forks were developed to fulfil the exacting conditions required. These forks have to be maintained at a constant temperature, and even in the methods of maintaining the control of the tem-perature of the heating chamber to the degree of accuracy required research work had to be undertaken. This may be surprising, but the fact is that the practical design or development of any piece of apparatus only advances up to that point where the apparatus meets existing needs; any further advance must come as a result of old standards being found insufficient.

Having solved the question of the frequency control of the facsimile gear, the question of the accurate measurement of frequency then became pressing, and considerable research work has been carried out to determine this to a sufficient degree of accuracy. Methods adopted are not yet perfect, but some considerable success has been obtained in the endeavour to control and measure frequency, there is, however, need of still more research before it can be said that this problem has been effectively solved. Measurements in the laboratories to one part in a million have been actually achieved, but what is wanted is apparatus that can be used commercially, and can be guaranteed to generate and maintain the frequency to this degree of accuracy, and other apparatus to measure such frequency correctly. When it is realized that all measurements must be referred to time as a standard, and that a clock with a rate of variation, either gain or loss, of one second a day means an accuracy of only one part in 86,400, some idea of the research work that has already been done in this field will be gained.

Again, the subject of facsimile involves the transformation of electrical energy to light energy, and vice versa, and it will therefore be realized that a considerable knowledge of physics is required in order to undertake research work of this nature. This type of investigation is, of course, undertaken by a research engineer of great experience with the assistance of other junior men, but these must also be men of sound scientific training and mathematical knowledge, in order that they can understand the problems set them. Men who have obtained first-class honours at a University or recognized technical college are the most suitable for this class of work. It is not essential that they should have had practical engineering experience in a Works or Electric Power Station, the knowledge they would have acquired of the use of tools and the running of machinery in the course of their practical training at their college or university being sufficient.

The link between research and commercial practice is undertaken by a section of the Technical Staff under the heading of Development. The development work chiefly consists in embodying the experimental results, or new inventions made by research engineers, into apparatus suitable for commercial exploitation. Other work which this section is called upon to perform consists in the modification of existing or standard types of apparatus to conform to the specification of some customer's requirements. Most of the orders that a wireless manufacturing concern receives are for stations or apparatus required by Government Departments or for broadcasting stations, run either by Governments or Corporations such as the B.B.C. Each Government, and in fact each Department of each Government, has its own ideas as to its requirements, and only in certain classes of apparatus is it possible to be sure that any standard design of apparatus will not have to be modified more or less to fulfil the requirements of an order. The modifications are often difficult to effect and the conditions and guarantees imposed are sometimes so severe as to entail a complete re-design of the apparatus as hitherto manufactured. This work generally falls on the Development Engineering Department to carry out. Engineers employed in this Department, while not requiring the same imaginative or inventive minds as research engineers, must also be men of sound scientific training ; they must have a thorough sense of design work from an engineer's point of view and ideas of design finish. They must have in addition the critical faculty for combining research ideals with commercial practicability. Suitable men for employment in development and design must have had experience in Works manufacture, so that they are familiar with Works processes, without which knowledge the designs they produce might be unnecessarily expensive to manufacture.

In the actual Works production of wireless apparatus a certain number of engineers are required, some for the design of detail parts of apparatus, as distinct from new development, others for the testing of wireless instruments, parts of apparatus, or complete wireless transmitters or receivers.   Such men must have had a sound technical training at some recognized college or institute, and preferably have had experience in an engineering works in a similar capacity : they do not require the same scientific knowledge as is essential in a research or development engineer, but they must have a sound knowledge of wireless principles.   Generally speaking, the work of the testing engineer is to a great extent routine work, but in a large wireless factory there are many varieties of apparatus to be tested, as well as all the parts and pieces to be tested separately before the set is completely assembled.

The next section of the engineering department deals with the preparation of the plans and designs of complete wireless stations, as distinct from the designs of individual apparatus ; this includes the designs of masts, aerials and buildings, the provision of the necessary power plant, switchboards and running machinery, and all the necessary cables and wiring for connecting up the different portions of the installation. Other work done by this Department includes the preparation of schedules and specifications to meet enquiries from potential customers, and the preparation of specifications for issue to manufacturers of plant not manufactured by the Wireless Company.   To carry out all this work a large staff of men is required.   Very complete drawings have to be prepared for each installation, for the use of the engineer who has to erect the station : for this a large number of draughtsmen is employed.   For the scheduling and drawing up of specifications, and the planning of the wireless station as a whole, a number of specially qualified engineers is employed.   These men must be experienced wireless engineers and cannot be drawn direct from colleges.   They are all men who have themselves erected wireless stations in different parts of the world, and therefore understand the practical requirements of station design, and what it is essential that the constructing engineer must be provided with.   The work they have to do is most varied ; rarely are two wireless stations alike, even if of the same power and type, local requirements entail essential differences.   It is on the schedules prepared by this Department that the estimates of cost are based.

To a young man desiring to take up wireless engineering as a career perhaps the most attractive section is that dealing with the erection of wireless stations. The engineer in the course of his career sees the world generally under pleasant conditions ; he has, if in charge of the work, great responsibilities and great opportunities of attracting special attention to his work. Finally, it is from this branch of wireless engineering that the majority of men are selected for the more highly paid administrative posts, or as Agents or Managers of allied or associated Companies abroad. The work they are required to do includes the choosing or approval of sites, the setting out of the installation on the site, the erection of buildings, masts, towers, aerials and feeder systems, the installation of prime movers for oil or steam, electrical generators, and motors, and all auxiliary apparatus, the assembly and adjustment of the wireless plant, both transmitters and receivers, the control apparatus, and sometimes land lines and power lines, and the complete equipment of the control office. In some cases the station may be for wireless telegraph purposes only, in others for telephony or broadcasting ; the engineer therefore has to understand the technique of wireless in its several branches as well as have a sound knowledge of general engineering. The type of man required for this class of work is quite distinct from the type required for research and development. The research engineer's chief recommendation will be his academic qualifications ; in the case of the constructional or contract engineer, while he must have a sound knowledge of wireless principles, his academic distinction is secondary to many other essentials. He should have an agreeable personality, should be diplomatic, and possess considerable tact, and if possible be of some social standing, as he will be required to deal with Government officials and foreign representatives, and should be able to mix in any society. He may even be required to negotiate for possible further contracts, involving considerable sums of money, and naturally such contracts may be lost or gained by the personality, tact, and discretion of the agent concerned. As most of his work will be abroad a knowledge of at least one foreign language is desirable ; French is the most important, after which come Spanish and German.

Another quality that the erecting engineer should possess is the ability to handle men of all grades ; he has to deal with the foreign labourer, excavating for foundations or pipe trenches, with mechanics of all trades, with operators of all nationalities, and with the foreign contractor and business man. In his hours of leisure he will meet all grades of society, and he must always remember that he is the local representative of his employers and that their prestige can be enhanced or suffer according as he conducts himself. As he will often be in sole charge of the execution of the contract some knowledge of bookkeeping is required, and some idea of the business side, such as the keeping of station accounts, the payment of labour, shipping and customs procedure, is essential. To a suitable man the life of an erecting engineer is most interesting ; it takes him out into the open air, he can get plenty of sport, shooting, fishing, hunting, if his tastes run that way, he sees foreign cities, wild virgin country, travels in liners to all parts of the world and in small vessels into little-known harbours, often he has to rely on his own resources or ingenuity to surmount unforeseen difficulties, he obtains longer holidays when he returns than those whose work keeps them at home, and when these are over he worries his head office until he is again sent to some other place abroad. Then, after years of travel and experience, there is the possibility before him of his employment at the head office of his Company in an administrative position, or in one of the sections of the engineering department dealing in installation or contract work ; finally he may be chosen as Chief Engineer or Manager of some associated Company abroad, or as the Agent of his Company in some foreign country.

There is another field for a wireless engineer in the care and maintenance of wireless stations already erected and carrying on a commercial wireless service. Maintenance engineers generally specialize on either the transmitting or the receiving side. A considerable number of maintenance engineers have earlier in their career been employed in the construction of wireless stations, but for the most part the staff manning the stations are drawn from young men who have passed through a technical college, and also had

experience in a works or electrical power station. The work
the young engineer has to do is very much a question of
routine. He has to keep the station running efficiently
during his hours of duty, see that all minor repairs and
renewals are effected, and he must know what to do when
anything goes wrong, how to trace a fault and how to remedy
it. When selected, he goes through a course of further
training at the Company's school, and then to one or other
of the wireless stations for practical training, until he is
reported to be capable of taking charge of a shift. Maintenance engineers live an easy life in agreeable conditions ;
the life can be compared to that of engineers employed in
electrical power stations, except that the latter are generally
built in squalid areas of cities or towns, whereas the wireless
stations are always built in the country.

There remains to describe the work of the head office
contract engineers. Every order for a wireless station or
piece of apparatus as received is passed to this section for
execution. They issue the specification and call for tenders,
through the Purchasing Department, for each piece of
material enumerated in the schedule ; it is their responsibility
to see that each detail is completed, tested, and shipped at
the required date to its destination. They are also required
to check all expenditure on a contract, and deal with all
correspondence in connection with it. Different engineers
deal with different types of orders, one section dealing with
ship installations, one with broadcasting installations, another
with military sets and aircraft wireless, yet another section
deals with large commercial wireless stations, These contract
engineers are all men of experience and most of them have
been drawn from the ranks of the constructional staff. A
man who has not had a wide engineering experience with the
Company would be of no use in this section.

Finally, there is the administrative section under the
direction of the Engineer-in-Chief, which determines the
general lines upon which each proposed wireless station
shall be planned and generally supervises the technical
work of the Company.

This chapter would not be complete without referring to
the financial prospects of a young engineer taking up wireless

as a career. A young man on first appointment is as a rule not of much use to the Company employing him until he has become familiar with the Company's methods and organization. Except in special cases a young engineer can expect to start with a salary of £150 to £200 a year and in the normal way he might expect small annual increases until he is considered fit for a more responsible position.

Naturally the class of work a man is fitted for governs the remuneration he receives and his future prospects. A first class research engineer may in time arrive at a four figure salary, though there are few that attain this. The constructional engineer, according to his abilities and length of service, receives a salary varying between £250 and £750 a year, but when sent on foreign contracts he can generally expect to receive a somewhat larger salary while so employed. He would also be paid reasonable living and travelling expenses actually incurred ; it is therefore possible for him to save most of his salary while abroad, at the same time living in reasonable comfort near his work.

The engineers employed at the head office receive salaries on about the same scale as constructional engineers ; only one or two at most can expect to obtain a salary of £1000 a year or more.

It can be seen therefore that a young man taking up wireless engineering as a career can make a living at his profession, but will not make a fortune. Very few engineers have gained riches directly by the exercise of their profession.

The rapid progress that has been, and is being continually made, in the material advancement of modern civilization is largely due to the work of engineers, yet the rewards they receive for inventions and discoveries, many of which during the past century have entirely altered the structure of society, are small compared to what the capitalist or business man gains in their exploitation. This is largely the fault of the training the engineer receives and his own reluctance to learn the principles of business and finance. Engineers as a class will remain the servants of capitalistic society, the hewers of wood and drawers of water for the Levitical priesthood of finance, until they realize that the business man is also a technician in another sense, and that without any knowledge of the principles of business or finance an engineer cannot be expected to raise himself to the position to which he might otherwise attain. Technical and engineering colleges make a great mistake in not including in their curriculum a series of lectures on book-keeping, accountancy, estimating, how to calculate overhead charges, how to understand a balance sheet and, particularly to impress on the student the economics of engineering, that the object he should always have in view is to produce the required result at the least possible expenditure. Many engineering companies are controlled by engineers who have realized the importance of a thorough business knowledge, and have taken steps to acquire this, but by far the larger number of engineers I have had to deal with have ignored the necessity of this training, and so missed the opportunities of high administrative posts, with the larger salaries attached to them.

Scientists and engineers as a rule find happiness and content in creative work and achievement rather than in the accumulation of riches. It is, however, essential to point out to the young man taking up engineering as a career the importance of his obtaining a business training as well as a technical one, if he has the ambition to be numbered among those who control or direct the particular industry with which he is associated.

Before concluding this chapter, it is as well to point out that, although a great industry in wireless has been built up, technical development in the different branches has by no means reached finality. Constant improvements are being made, increasing the efficiency of apparatus or circuits, or in the application of wireless to new services. The price of success is increasing attention to detail, and these improvements are chiefly due to the independent work of many different engineers, the cumulative effect of which has been of the greatest possible value in bringing the science and practice of wireless to its present stage in the search for perfection. There is still, however, a great deal to learn and many difficulties to overcome before many of the outstanding problems are successfully solved.

CHAPTER XXI

RESEARCH PROBLEMS

THE direction in which development and research in the field of electro-magnetic radiation can be forecast is divisible into two classes : the first is the perfection of methods at present in use or under development, whereas the second is the possibility of further developments in fields as yet barely entered by contemporary research. An indication has been made in a previous chapter as to the direction in which improvements and developments are likely to take place in the field of commercial communications. It is, however, only possible to speculate as to the lines along which discoveries may be made due to new and original research in that section of the band of electro-magnetic frequencies of which at present our knowledge is largely empirical. The increase in knowledge of electro-magnetic radiation, since the discoveries of the last century, has not been merely steady and constant, but has advanced by geometrical progression. The measurement of progress and the accumulation of knowledge gained can most easily be appreciated by an examination of the number of patents filed. A history of inventions is a history of progress, to which most civilized nations have contributed, and every great invention, such as the Fleming Valve and the Beam Aerial, marks one onward step. Inventions in one department of science suggest or facilitate inventions in another and every step becomes the basis for further progress. The advances in the methods of applied mathematics have provided means, whereby mechanical and physical sciences have made progress in their practical application, which would not have been possible without this aid to logical reasoning. To generalize, it may be said that all branches of scientific thought and achievement are correlated and extend beyond the ranges of their individual and immediate applications. The accumulation of scientific knowledge, applied to exploitation of the resources of nature, is available to every student. Every scientific event or technical invention is put on record, and this stock of accumulated knowledge serves as a reservoir from which fresh draughts of inspiration may be drawn. The means, whether mechanical or experimental, whereby scientific enquiry can be applied to any problem have also been largely extended, and can be classed with the ascertained facts of science, as part of the stock of knowledge equally available to the student.

Whereas the paths leading to the mass of accumulated facts and methods of investigation have been cut by a few great men and broadened by the tread of hundreds of men of lesser ability, the power to extend scientific knowledge requires a special gift of intellectual aptitude, a mind capable of combining the use of scientific methods of investigation, with the faculty of speculation, applied to matters which have not hitherto been fully investigated. There is a wide divergence between knowledge of the facts of science and the methods of their application, between the power of one man to use an invention and another to use a principle for the purpose of fresh discovery. The store of scientific knowledge is now so extensive that developments along one particular branch are only likely to advance under specialization. Whereas knowledge in the form of inventions or mathematical formula is ready to hand, it requires the same kind of brain to advance along new paths as that of the great scientists who made original discoveries with far less adequate means.

The wide field covered by electro-magnetic radiation offers the possibility of new discoveries of profound importance to humanity. Between the limits of the longest wireless wave that has been used, 30,000 metres, and the shortest cosmic ray of about one hundred billionth of a centimetre, consisting of about 60 octaves, only the wavelengths so far used in wireless communication and the light and infra red rays of heat have been extensively investigated. As regards the infra red rays, Rubens in Germany succeeded in isolating from purely thermal sources of heat rays of 1/3rd millimetre in wavelength, that is about nine octaves beyond the red end of the visible spectrum. The shortest Hertzian waves yet produced were reported by Nichols and Tear and were one hundredth of an inch in length, so these were shorter than the longest dark rays of heat. Observation of radiation from natural sources of heat and light, such as the sun, increases our knowledge of their particular properties, but until we can create and isolate waves, not recordable by human senses, and direct them with sufficient energy we cannot know to what degree many of the shortest wavelengths may affect human life either for good or ill.

There are already indications that ultra short wireless waves may be useful in other new directions. It has been noticed by workers on wireless short wave transmitting stations that the human body becomes instantly warm if standing in the field from the high frequency coil of a powerful transmitter, when the transmitter is emitting the shorter of the wavelengths used for telegraphic communication. This suggests the possibility of the use of short waves for therapeutic purposes, the alleviation of such diseases as lumbago, sciatica, and other rheumatic ills. It is possible that by a study of the effects of radiation of energy on the human body over a gradually decreasing length of wave information of value to medical science might be gleaned.

Recent electro-chemical research on food products and values in connection with the production of vitamins has shown that there exists a stage in the development of vitamins which has been called a " pre vitamin " and that the action of light on this substance results in the production of the vitamin. The effect of ultra violet rays converts the " pre vitamins " in the body and in food into vitamins. Here is an example of the creative and destructive effects of certain wavelengths on organic matters.

Dr. Bowden and Dr. Snow in the laboratory of physical Chemistry at Cambridge have shown that light changes a pre vitamin into a vitamin and may immediately afterwards change the vitamin into something else, but what is of especial interest to the student of the properties of electro-magnetic radiation is that the wavelength of the ray which creates the vitamin from the pre vitamin is different from that of the ray which destroys the vitamin. The wavelengths of both rays are in the band of ultra violet radiation. The chemical action of light depends on its absorption by the substance under its action. The problem is to discover what are the actual wavelengths in the ultra violet band which by absorption by the pre vitamin convert it into vitamin, and by absorption by the vitamin destroy it. Having determined the length of wave required for the conversion of the pre-vitamin, the second problem is to isolate this wavelength and exclude the destructive wavelength absorbed by the vitamin. The study of the chemical action of ultra violet rays upon pre vitamins and vitamins has helped to an understanding of the effect of the action of intense sunlight on the human body; research in this important field is likely to be of inestimable value in the near future.

Recently it has been reported that ultra short waves can be used to preserve meat, eggs, fruit and vegetables, using wavelengths of 1·5 metres downwards. The author has no knowledge of the process, nor of the type of transmitter used, nor whether the reputed effect is caused by the fundamental wave of the transmitter or one of its harmonics, but if true it opens up a fascinating field of speculation. Might it not be possible to destroy the bacteria of different diseases if means could be found to generate waves of a sufficient power of a wavelength of, say, twice the length of the particular bacteria and direct them on the human body?

As regards the many problems in wireless telegraph and telephone communication and its various applications, many well-known scientists and investigators are occupied in their elucidation, employed by one or other of the big wireless organizations in England, France, Germany, and America, and with the well-equipped laboratories in their control, and the specialized knowledge they have necessarily acquired, these organizations are well fitted to carry out such research work as concerns the development of their own businesses. The problems in connection with reflection from the upper strata of the atmosphere and the effect of sunlight, magnetic storms, and the changes in optima wavelengths due to seasonal effects, or solar storms, are all problems intimately affecting the reliability and continuity of wireless services, and as such are proper subjects for industrial organizations to investigate. Another field of research which is being undertaken by most wireless organizations is the possibilities and reliability of communication with ultra short waves (below 10 metres) down to 20 cms. or lower over varying distances and under different conditions.

The rationalization of industry, resulting in the creation of a number of national or international monopolies, whatever effect it may have on reducing costs and increasing sales, is not likely to be to the benefit of pure research. The natural tendency of a monopoly is the standardization of its products, and by the elimination of competition it is able to continue the marketing of an article when under competitive conditions that article might have been rendered obsolete by better designs produced by a competitor. The combination of competing firms into one organization obviates the necessity of each firm having its own research workers, and the number of men of scientific attainments required in the industry is reduced. Furthermore, the natural tendency of such organizations is to concentrate their research on utilitarian work for their immediate needs, and to discourage research and expenditure of a speculative character, also when trade is bad and economies have to be effected the temptation to reduce research expenditure is difficult to resist.

Development Companies, exploiting a new invention in its first practical form, such as the Marconi Company in the early days of wireless telegraphy, can only exist or expand by devoting their main efforts to technical improvements, involving substantial expenditure on research. It was due to the large sums spent year by year on research and experiment that the Marconi Company has always led in wireless development and its various practical applications. Its achievements in developing commercial wireless telegraphy up to the present day were largely due to the fact that it was not only a manufacturing Company but an operating Company also, owning and exploiting wireless stations, and its technical staff therefore were thoroughly acquainted with all the faults and failings of wireless communication both in principle and in detail. The Marconi Company, although it has sold its stations to the Imperial and International Communications

Ltd., still has the same facilities and opportunities as before, and it still continues as in the past to carry out research on problems of wireless communication. Neither the Marconi Company, nor any other industrial organization, can however justify expenditure on research in fields of a purely speculative character, and it is therefore a problem how to encourage research on work which holds out no apparent prospect of any immediate return. One possible solution would be to extend the facilities at the great universities where in the field of electro-magnetic radiation most of the theories and important discoveries have originated. Clerk-Maxwell, Hertz, Branly, Sir Oliver Lodge, Righi, Lord Rutherford, Sir Arthur Eddingtin, Sir Ambrose Fleming, to mention a few, all were or are Professors at different universities, and their contributions to our knowledge of electro-magnetic radiation were made due to the facilities available at the universities for experimental research. Much of the time of Professors at universities is, however, taken up in teaching, and the course of their research studies is in consequence seriously interfered with. What appears to be needed is that the Laboratories of Physics at these universities should be much more heavily endowed and that the State should make a substantial contribution towards their extension and upkeep and that such Professors who have shown their particular aptitude for certain lines of research should be relieved of academic duties to enable them to devote their full energies to the advancement of knowledge for the benefit of mankind.

The twentieth century has already brought about a profound change in our social life. It has witnessed the complete revolution of means of communication, the advent of the motor car and the aeroplane, the commercial application of wireless telegraphy and telephony, broadcasting and cinemas, and the birth of television. May we not hope that in the, as yet, unexplored fields of electro-magnetic radiation, discoveries will be made which will not only increase our scientific knowledge but also further harness nature to the service of mankind for the benefit of its health and welfare.

APPENDIX

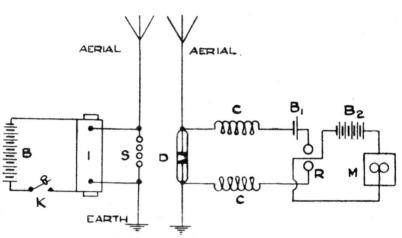

FIG. 1.—MARCONI'S EARLY TRANSMITTER AND RECEIVER
(see Chapter II, p. 15).

I, Induction Coil ; B, Battery ; K, Morse Key ; S, Spark Gap ; D, Coherer ; CC, Chokes ; B_1, B_2, Batteries ; R, Relay ; M, Recorder. Note that the Tapper Circuit has not been shown, for the sake of clearness.

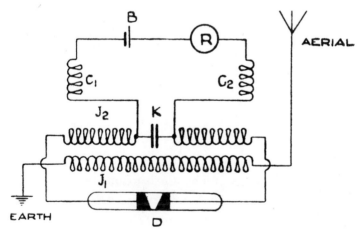

FIG. 2.—MODIFICATION OF MARCONI'S RECEIVER BY INTRODUCTION OF RECEIVING " JIGGER " (see Chapter II, p. 19).

D, Coherer ; J_1, Primary Winding of Jigger ; J_2, Secondary Winding of Jigger ; K, Condenser in centre of Jigger Secondary ; C_1, C_2, Chokes ; B, Battery ; R, Relay.

Fig. 1 shows diagrammatically the simple forms of transmitting and receiving circuits used by Marconi up to 1898. Fig. 2 shows the modification to the detector circuit after the invention of the receiving jigger, whereas Fig. 3 shows the arrangement of transmitting apparatus in Marconi's system of Syntonic Wireless Telegraphy under his Patent 7777, and Fig. 4 Marconi's receiving apparatus for syntonic reception. Figs. 5 and 6 show the arrangement of transmitting and receiving apparatus in Marconi's system of Multiple Syntonic Wireless Telegraphy.

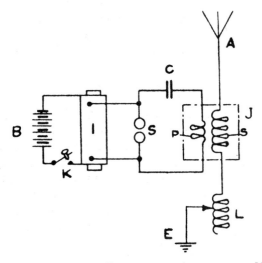

FIG. 3.—ARRANGEMENT OF TRANSMITTING APPARATUS IN MARCONI'S SYSTEM OF SYNTONIC TELEGRAPHY.

A, Aerial; E, Earth; L, Tuning Inductance; J, Jigger (Primary and Secondary); C, Condenser; S, Spark Gap; I, Induction Coil; K, Morse Key; B, Battery.

The particulars of the apparatus described in Marconi's patent for syntonic telegraphy are as follows :—

At the transmitting end the original arrangement of an aerial wire connected to one spark ball of an induction coil the other being earthed (now called plain aerial circuit) was exchanged for an aerial consisting of a pair of inductively coupled circuits. A condenser had one terminal connected to on spark ball of an induction coil and the other to the

primary winding of an oscillation transformer (called Transmitting Jigger). The opposite terminal of the primary winding of this transformer was joined to the other spark ball of
the induction coil. The secondary winding of the transmitting
jigger was inserted between the aerial wire and the earth
connection. In series with this aerial circuit an adjustable
coil was placed, known as an aerial tuning coil.

The oscillation transformer, or transmitting jigger, was
constructed on a wooden frame, over which was wound a
number of heavily insulated copper conductors of large cross
section, joined in parallel, making one turn of extremely low
resistance: in some cases two or more turns may be employed.
Over the primary winding a secondary winding of five or
more turns was wound. This secondary circuit was inserted
in the aerial circuit as above described. When connected up
as shown in Fig. 3, the oscillation transformer forms an
inductive coupling, between two circuits—one the primary
closed circuit of large capacity and low inductance, and the
other, containing the aerial, an open circuit of much smaller
capacity but much greater inductance. By the adjustment
of the variable inductance in the aerial circuit and by varying
the capacity of the condenser in the primary circuit the two
circuits are brought into resonance with each other.

When oscillations are set up in the close circuit by the
discharge of the condenser the energy stored up in the condenser is gradually drawn off and radiated from the open
aerial circuit. The closed circuit thus formed a reservoir of
energy and is in itself a slightly damped circuit, or persistent
oscillator. The open circuit is a good radiator and is kept
supplied with energy from the primary circuit. It is clear
therefore that a much more persistent train of oscillations
is set up in the aerial at each discharge than would be the
case where the storage of energy were that due to the aerial
only. The chief importance of this arrangement lies in the
accurate tuning of the primary and secondary circuits: when
the two circuits are exactly in tune together electrical oscillations set up in the primary circuit create other sympathetic
swings in the antenna circuit of similar nature and maximum
strength. By this arrangement the energy discharged into
the ether by the aerial at each spark was greatly increased

Q

and, what was equally important, each train of waves made to consist of a much larger number of waves, slowly decreasing in amplitude ; in other words, a long slightly damped train of waves rather than the very quickly quenched train of the simple original transmitting arrangement.

Turning now to the receiver, the diagram of connections of Marconi's syntonic receiver is shown in Fig. 4 :—

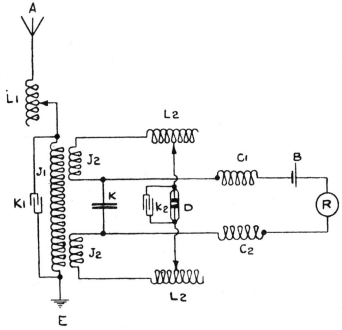

Fig. 4.—Arrangement of Receiving Apparatus in Marconi's System of Syntonic Wireless Telegraphy.

A, Antenna ; E, Earth ; L_1, Aerial Tuning Inductance ; J_1, J_2, Jigger Windings ; K_1, Aerial Circuit Tuning Condenser ; K, Jigger Condenser ; L_2, Tuning Inductances ; K_2, Adjustable Condenser ; D, Coherer ; C_1, C_2, Chokes ; B, Battery ; and R, Relay.

A is the aerial. At the bottom of the aerial there is an adjustable inductance L_1, connected to earth through the primary of a jigger J_1. Across the primary J_1 is placed a small variable condenser K_1. The secondary circuit J_2 is broken in the centre and a condenser K inserted. The outer terminals of the secondary circuit are connected through two small adjustable inductances L_2 with the terminals of the coherer D, across which is also placed another small variable condenser K_2. From the terminals of the jigger condenser K leads pass through two choking coils C_1 C_2 to the relay R and local cell B for working the relay. The Morse inker and the tapper circuit worked from the relay are not shown in the diagram.

To syntonize this receive with itself and with the incoming train of waves from the transmitter the two circuits, viz. the open circuit comprising the aerial inductance and jigger primary, and the closed circuit comprising the jigger secondary, the inductances L_2 L_2 and the condensers K and K_2 must be adjusted so that these two circuits are in resonance with each other and have the same natural time period of vibration as the transmitter circuits with which they are required to respond. These different frequencies are technically called " tunes " and the operation of putting the circuits into syntony is called tuning. Hence, in Marconi's syntonic system there were four circuits in tune with one another, viz. the condenser circuit and antenna circuit of the transmitter, and the antenna circuit and condenser circuit of the receiver. The condenser in the transmitter stored up at each charge a considerable amount of energy and on discharge imparted the energy in the aerial, setting up in the aerial prolonged trains of oscillations which gave up their energy to the ether. The receiver tuned to exactly the same wavelength is influenced by the sustained weak impulses received if the receiving aerial circuit is in tune, and in its turn imparts the received energy to the closed condenser circuit in association with it.

The receiving circuits can be set in electrical vibration better by a large number of electric waves, even of weak impulse, arriving on the receiving aerial at intervals exactly corresponding to the natural period of the vibrations of the receiving circuits themselves than by a single impulse or solitary wave. Hence with an accurately tuned receiver, although the ether may be full of electric waves impinging on every aerial, it will only respond to the wavelength to which it is tuned, provided the other impulses are not too powerful.

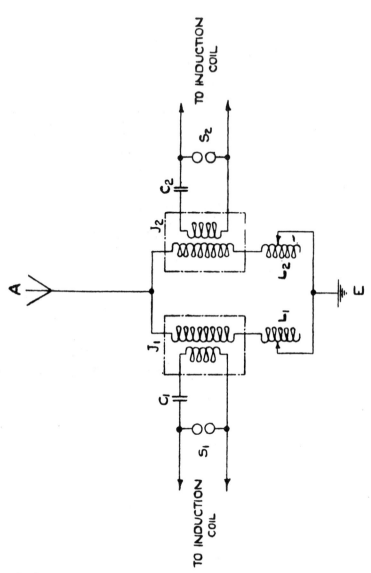

FIG. 5.—ARRANGEMENT OF TRANSMITTING APPARATUS IN MARCONI'S SYSTEM OF MULTIPLE SYNTONIC WIRELESS TELEGRAPHY.

A, Aerial ; J_1, J_2, Jiggers of two Transmitters ; L_1, L_2, Aerial Tuning Inductances for two Waves ; C_1, C_2, Condensers in closed Oscillatory Circuit of two Transmitters ; S_1, S_2, Spark Gaps two Transmitters.

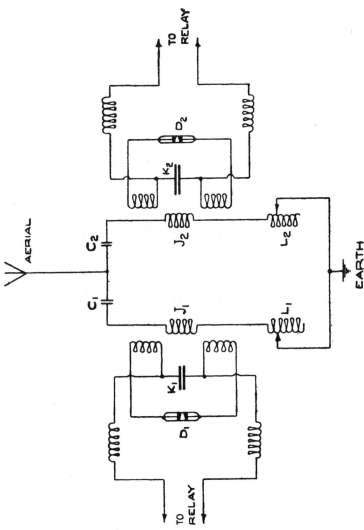

FIG. 6.—ARRANGEMENT OF RECEIVING APPARATUS IN MARCONI'S
SYSTEM OF MULTIPLE SYNTONIC WIRELESS TELEGRAPHY.

C_1, C_2, Aerial Condensers ; J_1, J_2, Jiggers ; L_1, L_2, Aerial Tuning Inductances ; K_1, K_2, Jigger Condensers ; D_1, D_2, Detectors.

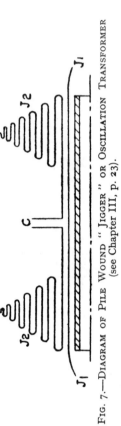

FIG. 7.—DIAGRAM OF PILE WOUND " JIGGER " OR OSCILLATION TRANSFORMER (see Chapter III, p. 23).

Where J_1 is a Single Layer of Wire Wound on a Glass Tube forming the Primary Winding, J_2 the Jigger Secondary Windings and C the Jigger Condenser.

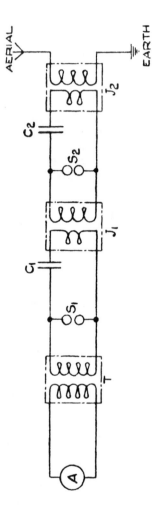

FIG. 8.—POLDHU TRANSMITTER (see Chapter III, p. 26).

A, Alternator 2000 volts; T, Transformer 2000–20,000 volts; S_1, First Spark Gap; C_1, Primary Condenser; J_1, Primary Oscillation Transformer or Jigger; S_2, Secondary Spark Gap; C_2, Secondary Condenser; J_2, Secondary Jigger.

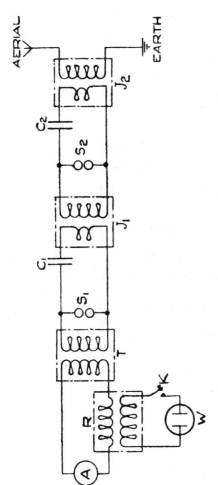

FIG. 9.—POLDHU TRANSMITTER WITH SIGNALLING TRANSFORMER, KEY AND
RESISTANCES (see Chapter III, p. 27).

The letters refer to the same details as in Fig. 8, but the Regulating Transformer
has now been inserted, shown by the letter " R ", while " K " represents the Signalling
Key and " W " the Adjustable Water Resistance.

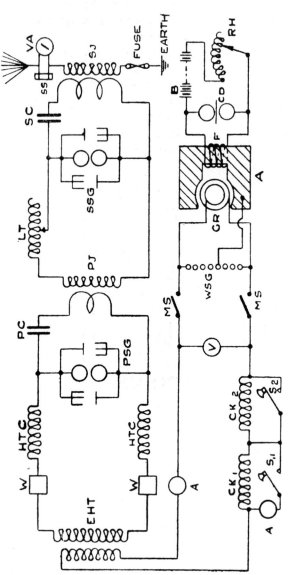

FIG. 10.—Actual Arrangement of Transmitting Plant at Poldhu on the Newfoundland Transatlantic Tests.

A, Alternator Frame; CR, Alternator Collector Rings; B, Battery; Rh, Rheostat; CD, Carbon Disc Protector across Field Windings; F, Alternator Field Windings; WSG, Wurtz Spark Gap Protector across Armature; MS, Main Switch; V, Voltmeter; A, Ammeter; CK1, CK2, Signalling Choking Coils; S1, S2, Signalling Switches; EHT, Transformer 2000–20,000 volt ratio; HTC, High Tension Inductance; WW, Wurtz Arrestors; PC, Primary Condenser; PSG, Primary Spark Gap fitted with Condenser Protectors; PJ, Primary Jigger; LT, Adjustable Tuning Inductance; SC, Secondary Condenser; SSG, Secondary Spark Gap with Protectors; SJ, Secondary Jigger; VA, Aerial Ammeter with SS Ammeter Shunt.

The two chokes CK1 and CK2 were used with the iron cores withdrawn, allowing 5·6 amperes to pass at 44 cycles, with an alternator voltage of 450 to 600 volts. The high tension transformers were connected in parallel, giving a ratio of one to ten. The high tension chokes HTC are additional chokes in the leads from the secondary windings of the transformers, the inductance in the Wurtz arrestors not being alone sufficient to prevent oscillations getting back to the transformer windings. The primary spark gap PSG was set for 7·5 mm., the maximum spark that the condenser could

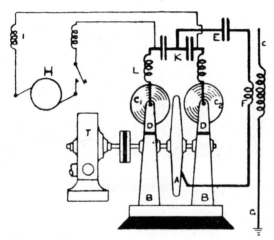

Fig. 11.—Disc Discharger (see Chapter IV, p. 45).

safely withstand. The primary capacity was 1·43 mfds. The primary jigger consisted of one primary turn comprised of fourteen 7/16 insulated wires in parallel. The secondary of the jigger was provided with ten and a half turns each of two 7/16 wires in parallel. The windings were wound on a wooden frame 21½ inches square and 6½ inches deep. The adjustable inductance LT consisted of forty turns each 1 foot long and the whole 40 feet were included in the circuit. The secondary spark gap SSG was set for 40 mm., with the condenser spark protector across it, so set that it would only function when a sudden surge of potential above normal took place. The secondary condenser SC was obtained from twenty-four stoneware condensers connected four in parallel, six in series, giving a capacity of ·037 mfd. A fuse was inserted in the earth lead ; this was used to test the amount of current in the aerial before and after each programme. The number of wires fused when everything was correctly adjusted, being nine strands of No. 31 gauge Platinoid wire twisted together.

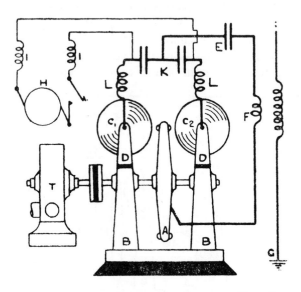

FIG. 12.—DISC DISCHARGER WITH STUDS ON MAIN DISC
(see Chapter IV, p. 46).

The dates when the Imperial Beam Stations were opened for service, after completing their acceptance trials, is given below together with their call signs and the wavelengths, used at that time. (See Chapter VIII, page 92.)

	Call Sign.	Date opened for Service.
Bodmin (England) . .	GBK (To Canada)	24/5 Oct. 1926.
Bodmin (England) . . .	GBJ (To S. Africa)	5 July 1927.
Grimsby (England) . .	GBH (To Australia)	8 April 1927.
Grimsby (England) .	GBI (To India)	5/6 Sept. 1927.
Drummondville (Canada)	CG (To England)	24/5 Oct. 1926.
Drummondville (Canada)	CJ (To Australia)	
Klipheuvel (South Africa) .	VNB	5 July 1927.
Ballan (Australia) . .	VIZ (To England)	8 April 1927.
Ballan (Australia) . .	VIY (To Canada)	
Kirkee (India) . .	VWZ	5/6 Sept. 1927.

ONGAR LONG WAVE AND SHORT WAVE TRANSMITTERS
(see Chapter IX).

Call Letters.	Wavelengths in Metres.	Power to Anodes in kw.	Services and Remarks.
GLC	9630	110	America (U.S.A.).
GLP	5332	25 ⎫	Both transmitters serve Barcelona,
GLO	4196	15 ⎭	Madrid, Vienna, Belgrade and other continental stations.
GLA	2950	10	Berne.
GLB	3950	5	Paris.
GMR	20·812 ⎫		*New York, beam or omni aerial.
GMU	33·88 ⎭	25	4 panel transmitter with two wavelengths.
GMQ	21·85 ⎫		*New York, beam or omni aerial.
GMS	39·525 ⎭	25	4 panel transmitter with two wavelengths.
GLU	14·51 ⎫		Nairobi, beam or omni aerial. 4
GLR	33·576 ⎭	25	panel transmitter with two wavelengths.
GMN	14·641 ⎫		Southern Rhodesia, beam or omni
GON	31·763 ⎭	25	aerial. 4 panel transmitter with two wavelengths.
GLQ	27·45	25	Rio de Janeiro.
GLS	16·133 ⎫		General services.
GMS	22·156 ⎪	40	Transmitter designed for rapid
GNS	25·93 ⎪		change to either of these wave-
GOS	32·34 ⎭		lengths.

* These two transmitters can work in parallel on the same beam aerial system, on 20·812 and 21·85 metres, the aerials having been designed for the mean of these two wavelengths.

TABLE I (see Chapter XVII, p. 189).

Frequency in Kilocycles per Second.	Approximate Wavelength in Metres.	Allocation to Services.
1,715– 2,000	175 –150	Mobile services, fixed services, amateurs.
2,000– 2,250	150 –133	Mobile services, fixed services.
2,250– 2,750	133 –109	Mobile services.
2,750– 2,850	109 –105	Fixed services.
2,850– 3,500	105 – 85	Mobile services, fixed services.
3,500– 4,000	85 – 75	Mobile services, fixed services, amateurs.
4,000– 5,500	75 – 54	Mobile services, fixed services.
5,500– 5,700	54 – 52·7	Mobile services.
5,700– 6,000	52·7 – 50	Fixed services.
6,000– 6,150	50 – 48·3	Broadcasting.
6,150– 6,675	48·8 – 45	Mobile services.
6,675– 7,000	45 – 42·8	Fixed services.
7,000– 7,300	42·8 – 41	Amateurs.
7,300– 8,200	41 – 36·6	Fixed services.
8,200– 8,550	36·6 – 35·1	Mobile services.
8,550– 8,900	35·1 – 33·7	Mobile services, fixed services.
8,900– 9,600	33·7 – 31·6	Fixed services.
9,500– 9,600	31·6 – 31·2	Broadcasting.
9,600–11,000	31·2 – 27·3	Fixed services.
11,000–11,400	37·2 – 26·3	Mobile services.
11,400–11,700	26·3 – 25·6	Fixed services.
11,700–11,900	25·6 – 25·2	Broadcasting.
11,900–12,300	25·2 – 24·4	Fixed services.
12,300–12,825	24·4 – 23·4	Mobile services.
12,825–13,350	23·4 – 22·4	Mobile services, fixed services.
13,350–14,000	22·4 – 21·4	Fixed services.
14,000–14,400	21·4 – 20·8	Amateurs.
14,400–15,100	20·8 – 19·85	Fixed services.
15,100–15,350	19·85– 19·55	Broadcasting.
15,350–16,400	19·55– 18·3	Fixed services.
16,400–17,100	18·3 – 17·5	Mobile services.
17,100–17,750	17·5 – 16·9	Mobile and fixed services.
17,750–17,800	16·9 – 16·85	Broadcasting.
17,800–21,450	16·85– 14	Fixed services.
21,450–21,550	14 – 13·9	Broadcasting.
21,550–22,300	13·9 – 13·45	Mobile services.
22,300–23,000	13·45– 13·1	Mobile and fixed services.
23,000–28,000	13·1 – 10·7	Not reserved.
28,000–30,000	10·7 – 10	Amateurs and experiments.
30,000–56,000	10 – 5·35	Not reserved.
56,000–60,000	5·35– 5	Amateurs and experiments.
above 60,000	below 5	Not reserved.

Table II shows the bands restricted to fixed services only and from a point of view of interest a column is given showing the maximum possible number of wavelengths in each section if each were separated by 10,000 cycles, while further columns give the approximate wavelength separation and the corresponding possible number of wavelengths on the suggestion that the width of band should be obtained by taking the square root of ten times the frequency. From these it can be seen that on the shorter wavelengths the width of allowable band would be larger than 10,000 cycles, while on the longer wavelengths the width of band becomes narrower.

TABLE II

No. of Band.	Frequency in Kilocycles.	Approximate Wavelength in Metres.	Possible No. of Stations with 10,000 Cycles Separation.	Frequency Separation on Square Root Basis.	No. of Separate Wavelengths.
1	2,750– 2,850	109 –105	10	5·3	19
2	5,700– 6,000	52·7 –50	30	7·64	39
3	6,675– 7,000	45 –42·8	32·5	8·16	39
4	7,300– 8,200	41 –36·6	90	8·8	102
5	8,900– 9,500	33·7 –31·6	60	9·6	64
6	9,600–11,000	31·2 –27·3	140	10·15	137
7	11,400–11,700	26·3 –25·6	30	10·75	28
8	11,900–12,300	25·2 –24·4	40	11	36
9	13,250–14,000	22·4 –21·4	65	11·7	55
10	14,400–15,100	20·8 –19·85	70	12·15	58
11	15,350–16,400	19·55–18·3	105	12·6	83
12	17,800–21,450	16·85–14	365	14	260
			1037·5		920

The total number of stations that would be possible if each station had one wavelength with an exclusive right to a band of 10,000 cycles only amounts to 1037 and only to 920 if the other method of determining the width of band were adopted. There are other bands of wavelengths within which fixed stations for point to point services may be employed, but these bands are not exclusively reserved for fixed stations. They are also shared with mobile services and in the case of two of the bands with amateurs.

TABLE III

	Frequency in Kilocycles.	Approximate Wavelength in Metres.	Possible Number of Stations.		
1	1,715– 2,000	175 –150	28·5	Amateurs 4·3	66
2	2,000– 2,250	150 –133	25	4·6	54
3	2,850– 3,500	105 – 85	65	5·6	116
4	3,500– 4,000	85 – 75	50	Amateurs 6·1	82
5	4,000– 5,500	75 – 54	150	6·9	217
6	8,550– 8,900	35·1 – 33·7	35	9·3	39
7	12,825–13,350	23·4 – 22·4	53·5	11·4	46
8	17,100–17,750	17·5 – 16·9	65	13·2	49
9	22,300–23,000	13·45– 13·1	70	15	46
			541		755

This list gives another 541 stations on the 10,000 cycle separation basis, bringing the total up to 1578, or based on a separation calculated by the square root of ten times the frequency the total number would be 1675, but of this last list many of the wavelengths are used by ships, and as it is considerably more difficult for a variety of reasons to ensure a high degree of constancy of frequency in ship installations, fixed stations avoid the shared bands for fear of interference, unless forced into them for want of space.

The lists in Tables II and III in reality give the total possible number of wavelengths and not the total stations, the number of which if allocated exclusive wavebands would be considerably smaller. Table IV sets out the bands of wavelengths allocated to fixed services, the theoretical number of wavelengths available, again on the arbitrary assumption of a 10,000 cycle separation, and the number of allocations of wavelengths in each band to fixed stations.

TABLE IV.

No. of Band.		Frequencies in Kilocycles.	Approximate Wavelengths in Metres.	Possible Number of Stations with 10,000 Cycles Separation.	No. of Wavelengths Registered 1932 by fixed Stations.
6	1	2,750– 2,850	109 –105	10	33
11	2	5,700– 6,000	52·7 –50	30	317
14	3	6,675– 7,000	45 –42·8	32·5	247
16	4	7,300– 8,200	41 –36·6	90	685
19	5	8,900– 9,500	33·7 –31·6	60	307
21	6	9,600–11,000	31·2 –27·3	140	513
23	7	11,400–11,700	26·3 –25·6	30	127
25	8	11,900–12,300	25·2 –24·4	40	192
28	9	13,350–14,000	22·4 –21·4	65	204
30	10	14,400–15,140	20·8 –19·85	70	185
32	11	15,350–16,400	19·55–18·3	105	221
36	12	17,800–21,450	16·85–14	365	481
				1037·5	3512

Table V shows the number of wavelengths already registered by fixed and mobile stations in the shared band.

TABLE V.

No. of Band.		Frequencies in Kilocycles.	Approximate Wavelengths in Metres.	Possible Number of Stations with 10,000 Cycles Separation.	No. of Wavelengths Registered 1932 by Fixed Stations.
3	1	1,715– 2,000	175 –150	28·5	62
4	2	2,000– 2,250	150 –133	25	69
7	3	2,850– 3,500	105 –85	65	503
8		3,500– 4,000	85 –75	50	162
9		4,000– 5,500	75 –54	150	1199
18		8,550– 8,900	35·1 –33·7	35	428
27		12,825–13,350	23·4 – 22·4	52·5	251
34		17,100–17,750	17·5 – 16·9	65	218
39		22,300–23,000	13·45– 13·1	70	28
				541	2920

TABLE VI

No. of Band.	Frequency in Kilocycles.	Possible No. of Stations with 10,000 Cycles Separation.	Actual No. of Stations Registered.	Power in Kilowatts to Aerial.							
				Below ½ kw.	From ½ to 2 kw.	From 2 to 5 kw.	From 5 to 10 kw.	From 10 to 25 kw.	From 25 to 50 kw.	Above 50 kw.	Unrecorded or in Project.
6	2,750— 2,850	10	33	18	2	1	—	—	—	—	12
11	5,700— 6,000	30	303	192	40	13	6	3	8	5	36
14	6,675— 7,000	32·5	303	118	46	15	9	12	4	37	62
16	7,300— 8,200	90	685	274	67	121	29	27	21	18	128
19	8,900— 9,500	60	307	87	35	39	18	19	13	29	67
21	9,600—11,000	140	513	153	65	56	22	50	17	17	133
23	11,400—11,700	30	127	48	11	4	14	6	3	3	38
25	11,900—12,300	40	192	94	15	13	8	17	7	2	36
28	13,350—14,000	65	204	50	22	21	19	13	8	39	32
30	14,400—15,100	70	185	29	29	40	15	24	6	14	28
32	15,350—16,400	105	221	33	22	79	21	13	2	26	25
36	17,800—21,450	365	481	19	37	106	83	86	24	59	67
	Totals	1037	3554	1115	391	508	244	270	113	249	664

Wavelengths and Stations in the Shared Bands.

No. of Band.	Frequency in Kilocycles.	Possible No. of Stations with 10,000 Cycles Separation.	Actual No. of Stations Registered.
3	1,715— 2,000	28·5	62
4	2,000— 2,250	25	69
7	2,850— 3,500	65	503
8	3,500— 4,000	50	162
9	4,000— 5,500	150	1199
18	8,550— 8,900	35	428
27	12,825—13,350	52·5	251
34	17,100—17,750	65	218
39	22,300—23,000	70	28
		541	2920